THE OPEN UNIVERSITY

Social Sciences: a third level course
Research Methods in Education and
the Social Sciences

Block 2B   Beginning Research

DE304 Research Methods in Education and The Social Sciences

Central Course Team
Michael Wilson (Chairman)
John Bynner
(Chairman, Production)
Judith Calder
Peter Coxhead
Jeff Evans (on secondment
    from Middlesex Polytechnic)
Martyn Hammersley
Jane Henry (IET)
Fred Lockwood (IET)
Robert Peacock
Roger Sapsford
Keith Stribley (Course Assistant)
Betty Swift
Melanie Bayley (Editor)
Giles Clark (Editor)
Aldwyn Cooper (SCS)
Peter Cox (SCS)
Martyn Haywood (SCS)
Vic Lockwood (BBC)
Ken Patton (BBC)
Tag Taylor (Designer)
Eleanor Thompson (Project Control)

External Assessor
Marie Jahoda CBE
(Emeritus Professor of Social
Psychology, University of Sussex)

Internal Consultants
Christopher Brook
Michael Drake
Judith Greene
Andrew Pollard
Adrian Thomas

External Consultants
Liz Atkins, Medical Research Council
Paul Atkinson, University College, Cardiff
Martin Bulmer, London School of Economics
Wyn Lewis, University of Warwick
Cathie Marsh, University of Cambridge
Peter Martin, University of Manchester
Desmond Nuttall, Middlesex Examining Board
Bram Oppenheim, London School of Economics
Albert Pilliner, University of Edinburgh
David Romney, Laurentian University, Ontario

Acknowledgements

The Course Team are indebted to the following for their assistance: John Murrell and John Bibby for their comments on the draft material; Patrick Miller for preparing the Glossary; David Short and the students who developmentally tested the course; Professor Jim Davis for invaluable help with the survey analysis section; Barrie Hedges, Jane Wainwright, Lynn and Steve Murgatroyd, and Angela Summerfield for contributions to the shaping of Block 2; Paul Smith for preparing the course library guide; Michael Levers and Tim Chard for photographic work; Keith Howard for graphic illustrations; Liz Joseph, Cathy Bayntun, Mary Cox, Betty Gregory and Ann Boomer, who were the course secretaries; Pat Coombes and Glenna White who helped with the preparation of drafts for publishing. Many others, both from the Open University and elsewhere, have helped to realize this course – to them our thanks.

The Open University Press
Walton Hall, Milton Keynes
MK7 6AA

First published 1979. Reprinted 1981, 1986.

Designed by the Graphic Design Group of the Open University.

Printed in England by Staples Printers St Albans Limited at The Priory Press.

ISBN 0 335 07437 5

This text forms part of an Open University course. The complete list of the course appears at the end of this text.

For general availability of supporting material referred to in this text, please write to Open University Educational Enterprises Limited, 12 Cofferidge Close, Stony Stratford, Milton Keynes, MK11 1BY, Great Britain.

Further information on Open University courses may be obtained from the Admissions Office, The Open University, P.O. Box 48, Walton Hall, Milton Keynes, MK7 6AB.

2.2

Part 4   Descriptive Statistics

Prepared by R.W. Lewis for the Course Team

Block 2 Part 4

Contents

Aims

Most empirical research studies in the social sciences tend to produce large quantities of numerical information or data. A report of one such study is given in Appendix 3 of Volume 2 of the Plowden Report. It concerns a national survey of parental attitudes and circumstances related to school and pupil characteristics whose aim was to investigate the links between home circumstances and child's educational progress. In the main survey over 3000 parents of primary school children were interviewed. The questionnaire comprised 64 separate questions and many of these had more than one part to be answered. Thus the survey collected a minimum of 192 000 items of information.

Looked at in this light, the problem is immediate and obvious. Given such a large amount of data, how does a researcher attempt to extract the kinds of information which will help answer his initial *research questions* and hypotheses? Even by looking at one variable at a time, very little can be deduced from the data in their 'raw' state – it would be rather difficult, for example, to come to any conclusion about the age structure of parents simply from attempting to 'read' a long list of 3000 ages. And correspondingly it would be even more difficult to make any sense of the interrelationship between any two variables, say social class and family income.

research question

The data have to be reduced to manageable proportions, and need to be summarized in such a way that the essential differences and relationships stand out clearly. So, the initial steps in data analysis invariably involve the use of relatively simple *descriptive methods* such as the presentation of data in tables and diagrams and the calculation of *summary measures* of location, dispersion and correlation or association. These methods are known as *descriptive statistics*.

descriptive methods, summary measures, descriptive statistics

The aim of descriptive statistics is to provide the researcher with a basic understanding of the data, and many analyses proceed no further than the use of these descriptive methods. In many respects, both conceptually and in practice, they can be looked upon as forming the basic tools and building-blocks of *data analysis*, raising questions which might indicate the need for complex methods. In addition, there is always the problem of communicating the results of complex analysis to non-specialist or lay readers, and descriptive statistics are useful in this respect.

data analysis

The relative simplicity of descriptive statistics should not lead you to suppose that their use and interpretation is free of difficulties. As with all data analysis, there is the problem of imperfectly observed data being fitted to ideal abstract models. Each method has characteristics of its own, being defined in a special way, relying on a given set of assumptions, and designed to answer a given question of the data. Even with such apparently simple methods, if a researcher is not sufficiently familiar with the constraints on their uses, they can easily be employed so as to give misleading results and misleading interpretations. It must always be remembered that a method or technique of analysis should not be used in a mechanical way, but that its possible use must always be considered within the framework of the overall purpose and context of the analysis.

The primary aim of this unit is to give you a basic understanding of the concepts and ideas of descriptive statistics and some guidance as to when and how the various methods might be useful. To this end the numerical examples are kept as simple and straightforward as possible. The computational complexities which can arise in practical research will be dealt with in conjunction with the computer analysis of the larger data set incorporated in the Interactive Data Analysis (IDA) program which has been prepared for the course by SCS.

Study Guide

Your main aim in studying this text is to achieve the objectives which are listed at the end. This is quite a formidable list and might seem especially daunting to those of you who have never met descriptive statistics before. In fact you have already begun to acquire the skills of summarizing, describing and interpreting data in your study of Part 3. There you were given the opportunity to comment upon trends and to draw comparisons from sets of data between sexes and age groups, different time periods and geographical regions in terms of raw figures, totals and percentages. This Part of the Block introduces you to a systematic approach to the summarizing of data sets; a familiarity with various data handling techniques is a prerequisite for inferential analysis and causal modelling which will be introduced in Blocks 6 and 7.

One reason for including this Part in a Block concerned with getting started in research is that it follows logically from the use of published statistics to generate research ideas and formulate operational hypotheses. Very often an operational hypothesis will be framed in precise (statistical) terms: for example, you might be interested in the effect over time of taxation policies on the distribution of incomes; a hypothesis might be framed in terms of the specific differences from time to time, or between different occupational groups, in the values of the standard deviations or quartile dispersion coefficients of observed income distributions. Much research is concerned with establishing the existence and strength of relationships between variables such as 'educational attainment' and 'social class'. Relationships can be summarized in terms of an appropriate measure of correlation, or correlation coefficient, and an operational hypothesis may take the precise form concerning the observed or expected value of a correlation coefficient.

The whole of the text which follows is relevant to the achievement of the objectives. The text has worked examples and 40 SAQs; you should work through these carefully and be sure you understand what each is about. The answers to SAQs often contain a lot of additional information which supplements the exposition provided in the text and should help you to understand more clearly the principles and procedures being illustrated.

The examples and questions provided in the text have been designed to be as straightforward as possible with a minimum of data handling, so that the techniques of manipulating figures do not get in the way of the basic ideas. All the examples are based upon the same data set which represents just thirty observations on each of seven variables from the results of the Plowden research; this data set is reproduced in the Appendix. Most of the exercises require you to select ten observations or less from the same data set and to perform calculations on the ungrouped data. (The distinction between grouped and ungrouped data sets is explained in paragraphs 2.2 and 2.3 below.)

Often you will have to summarize and analyse large amounts of data which have been tabulated in grouped frequency form; you will then need to understand how to use the techniques covered here in that context. Sometimes your data analysis will be carried out automatically by computer and it will be sufficient for you to appreciate and understand the principles on which the analysis is carried out. At other times you will inevitably be involved in handling fairly large quantities of data by the long-hand method using pencil, paper and electronic calculator, when you will need to be able to carry out all the computations yourself.

These skills may not be easy to achieve, but they are not impossible to master. You should expect your progress to be slow at first and do not be put off if it seems to be more difficult than you expected. Try to work through the text more than once, if you have the time, and come back to it again whenever you have difficulty in remembering or applying the ideas contained in it, especially when you are studying Blocks 6 and 7. Revision and practice are important aids to learning new skills. The amount of practice which can be incorporated in the text is limited to just the 40 SAQs, but further practice is available through the CICERO tutorials and the IDA program which allows you to compute summary statistics for the larger Plowden data set taken from the follow-up survey.

Anyone who is now confident and fluent in the use of descriptive statistics and elementary data analysis knows that ideas and techniques which once seemed almost impossibly difficult to make sense of do become more familiar and less formidable with every new application. You are bound to share a similar experience and the sense of satisfaction gained through your achievement will make all your efforts worthwhile.

1 Scales of Measurement

1.1 In employing a statistical method to analyse a set of data, the assumptions underlying the construction of that method are of crucial importance. One of the constraints revolves around the level or *scale of measurement* of the data; for, in general, given methods can only be used if the data conform to a scale of measurement assumed by the method. This section will outline the basic principles involved, and you will come to a more detailed and wider discussion of the problem of measurement in the social sciences in Block 4, Part 1 and particularly Block 5, Part 2.

scale of measurement

1.2 Everyone, in everyday life, is constantly *categorizing* social and physical phenomena. We distinguish between different religions – Christianity, Buddhism, Hinduism; different types of houses – detached, semi-detached, terraced; different modes of transport – car, train, bus; and different towns – London, Margate, Oldham. We sometimes say that we may prefer one type of music to another; a teacher may rank the children in a class in terms of ability; a customer may prefer Brand X to Brand Y; also we constantly use pounds (£) and pence to say that one income is twice another, or miles to compare distances or years from birth to compare ages, or degrees Fahrenheit to compare temperatures. We are, in effect, constantly measuring the world around us. At its simplest, then, *measurement* is a procedure for classifying individuals, groups or other units and putting them into previously defined *categories*. A *variable*, in these terms, is any characteristic which has two or more possible categories.

categorization

measurement

category, variable

1.3 Measurement is obviously an intrinsic element in any research in the social sciences. Take for example, the 1964 National Survey described in Volume 2 of the Plowden Report, which collected information from the parents of children in primary schools. In order to assess the feasibility of their *operational hypotheses* concerning the educational attainment of primary school children, the researchers collected information on the child's age and country of birth, the father's occupation, the parents opinions on whether pupils of different abilities should be in the same class, on parental discipline, on which type of secondary school they would like their child to go to, and so on; and in each case, various categories of answer were possible.

operational hypothesis

1.4 In research such as this, unlike everyday life, the categories of the variables are very often assigned numerals or numbers. Secondary schooling, for example, may be given as '1' for Grammar, '2' for Secondary Modern, '3' for others; a father's attitude to his child may be classified as '1' for strict, '2' moderate, '3' fairly lenient, '4' very lenient, with an implied ranking of strictness; age is given as 25, 35 or 45 years. The statistical analysis of such data operates not on the categories themselves but on the numerals or numbers attached to them, and therefore great care has to be taken in understanding their meaning. Some mathematical operations make sense in the above examples and others do not – we cannot 'add' a Grammar school and a Secondary Modern school (i.e. '1' + '2') to obtain the 'other' type of school '3'; whereas it does make sense to say that the difference in age between a 35 and 25 year old is the same as that between a 45 and a 35 year old. In the former case the 'numerals' are simply labels, in the latter they have quantitative meaning and are 'numbers'.

1.5 Thus, in the social sciences we require a stricter definition of measurement, but it is now generally accepted that, in its broadest sense, measurement is the assignment of numerals to objects or events according to rules. It is the 'rules' which tell us which kinds of statistical analysis can be used on a given set of data. From the above definition, four different scales of measurement can be identified – *nominal*, *ordinal*, *interval* and *ratio*. Some writers have introduced other scales, but a knowledge of these four will be sufficient for our purposes.

Nominal Scales

1.6 *Nominal scales* are the simplest form of measurement. A variable measured on a nominal scale is one which is divided into two or more categories: e.g. sex is categorized as male or female; regions into North, South, East or West; a question as to whether a family owns a car can be answered 'yes' or 'no'. It is simply a sorting operation in which all individuals or units or answers can be placed in one category or another (i.e. the categories are *exhaustive*). The essential characteristic of a nominal scale is that we can say, in terms of a given variable, that one individual is different from another, that the categories *discriminate*. There is no implication of order, or preference, simply difference. This characteristic of classification is fundamental to all scales of measurement.

nominal scale

1.7 As mentioned above, it is often the case that numerals are assigned to the categories of a nominal variable, so that we might have:

Male   1

Female   0

It must be emphasized that these numerals are merely labels and could just as well have been 10 and 247. They do not have the properties of numbers in that they cannot be added, subtracted, multiplied or divided, any more than these arithmetical operations can be meaningfully used on, say, car registration numbers.

Ordinal Scales

1.8 *Ordinal scales* have all the properties of a nominal scale, but, in addition, categories can be ordered along a *continuum* in terms of a given criterion. Given three categories, A, B and C, on an ordinal scale we might be able to say, for example, that A is greater than B and B is greater than C (i.e. $A > B > C$) or, alternatively, C is less than B and B is less than A (i.e. $C < B < A$). Criteria other than 'greater than' or 'less than' can be used – such as larger, bigger, more important, more beautiful, more hostile, warmer, cleaner, more intelligent and many others. Numerous examples of variables measured on ordinal scales occur in the social sciences. One was given above in terms of the strictness or leniency of a father towards his child. Other examples would be reading levels in school, ranks in the armed services, the classification of university degrees. Traditionally, social class, or socio-economic group, however precisely measured, has to be looked upon as an ordinal variable.

ordinal scale, continuum

1.9 As with nominal scales, numerals are again often assigned to the different categories. Thus we could have army ranks in terms of status as a sergeant having higher status than a corporal having a higher status than a private. These could be labelled respectively $3 > 2 > 1$. But the only property of numbers that these labels possess is that 3 is greater than 2 is greater than 1. The numbers do not imply that the difference in status between a sergeant and corporal is the same as the difference between a corporal and a private or that $1 + 2 = 3$, i.e. a private plus a corporal equals a sergeant. On an ordinal scale, we can simply distinguish order, and say nothing about the distance between the categories. For all practical purposes we could substitute 100, 50 and 10 for 3, 2 and 1.

Interval and Ratio Scales

1.10 The third scale of measurement is the *interval scale*. It has all the characteristics of an ordinal scale, but in addition its categories are defined in terms of *standard units* of measurement. This means essentially that the distances or intervals between categories can be measured in terms of the units, for a number can be assigned to an object that equals the number of units of

interval scale

standard unit

measurement, equivalent to the amount of the property possessed. In formal terms we can say not only that A, B and C are distinct categories, and that $A > B > C$, but also that $(A - B) = (B - C)$ or that $A - C = 2(A - B)$. However, an interval scale is one where there is no absolute zero point – it can be placed anywhere along a continuum; this means that although we can add and subtract, we cannot multiply and divide.

1.11   There are very few examples of pure interval scales. Temperature as measured on a Centigrade or Fahrenheit scale provides one example. Here the 'zero' is arbitrary and although the difference between 60°F and 50°F is the same as the difference between 50°F and 40°F, it makes no sense to say that 64°F is twice as warm or hot as 32°F.

1.12   *Ratio scales* have all the characteristics of an interval scale but in addition have a *fixed zero*, and there are obviously many examples such as age, weight, height, length, income, expenditure, number of children, and others. In each we have a concept of zero – no children, no income, etc. This means that we can use all the usual arithmetical operations on such data. A family with 2 children has twice as many children as another with 1 child; an 8 year old is half the age of a 16 year old; and so on.

ratio scale, fixed zero

1.13   *Interval* and *ratio variables* – where standard units can be identified – are an important step up from *nominal* or *ordinal variables* and a wealth of mathematical and statistical methods can be employed in their analysis. The different statistical methods you will come across in later sections are related to these different scales of measurement, in that there is usually a correspondence between the mathematical assumptions of method and the assumptions of the scale of measurement. Certain methods require only categorized data and can be used on a nominal variable. Others assume *rank ordering* and can be used on ordinal scales. Care must always be taken to match the methods used with the scale of measurement of the variables and not to use a method which implies a higher scale of measurement than the variable allows. But you must remember that one cannot always in practice apply the criteria for the various scales in a clear-cut or simple manner. While many variables in social research fall naturally onto one or other scale of measurement, others, such as indices of most descriptions or 'attitude' scales, are subject to argument particularly on the ordinal/interval boundary. In addition many statistical methods are 'robust' in allowing deviations from their strict assumptions. This point will be expanded in Block 5, Part 2.

interval variable, ratio variable, nominal variable, ordinal variable

rank order

1.14   The scales of measurement themselves comprise an ordinal scale, as the assumptions underlying a nominal scale are a subset of those of an ordinal scale, and those of an ordinal scale are a subset of those of an interval scale. This means that any statistical methods which can be used on nominal variables can also be used on ordinal variables; any methods developed for ordinal variables can be used for interval or ratio variables; but methods developed for interval or ratio variables cannot strictly be used for any of the others.

1.15   In reading textbooks and other discussions of measurement in the social sciences, you need to be aware that the terminology used is not always consistent. We have defined a *variable* as any characteristic capable of being measured on any one of the four scales of measurement. In some texts you will find a distinction drawn between *qualitative variables* or *qualitative measurement* and *quantitative variables* or *quantitative measurement;* the former usually refer to data measurement on nominal or ordinal scales and the latter to interval or ratio scales. Again, you may well find that the term variable is restricted to characteristics which can be measured on an interval or ratio scale, while those on a nominal scale are termed *attributes* and those on an ordinal scale are termed *ordered attributes*.

qualitative variable or qualitative measurement, quantitative variable or quantitative measurement, attribute, ordered attribute

1.16   Finally, we need to draw one further distinction – that between 'continuous' and 'discrete' variables. A *discrete variable* is one which can take only a limited number of distinct values, scores or categories. Thus a variable such as number of children in a family can only take the values 0, 1, 2, 3, 4, etc. A single family cannot have 2.3 or $4\frac{1}{2}$ children; the units are *integers* and indivisible. But you might note that a statistical operation such as *'averaging'* can produce a meaningful 'average' family size of 2.35. Nominal variables are discrete by definition; as are ordinal variables such as a social class grading unless the researcher can reasonably postulate an underlying continuum. A *continuous variable* is one which can reasonably, and within the constraints of measurement, be supposed to take any fractional or decimal value between any two integers. Age can easily be thought of in this way. In principle, given any two ages however close, it is possible to find a third which lies in between. Other variables, such as income, can be treated as being continuous for all practical purposes even though there is usually a finite lower value such as, for example, a half-penny ($\frac{1}{2}$ p) in the currency of the United Kingdom.

discrete variable

integer, average

continuous variable

SAQ 1

Look at the seven variables shown in the data set in the Appendix and say, for each, whether it is measured on a nominal, ordinal, interval or ratio scale. You will need to refer to the notes which follow the table and which explain the variable codes.

e.g. The first variable represents 'social class' with six categories from Social class I coded 1 to Social class V coded 6. On the assumption that SCI is higher than SCII that II is higher than III, and so on, this variable can be considered to be *ordinal*. It clearly qualifies as a nominal variable since the six categories have clearly defined codes, but it cannot be considered to be interval since it is impossible to say that the difference between SCI and SCII is the same as the difference between SCIV and SCV, nor can we say the difference between SCI and SCIV is three times as important as the difference between SCI and SCII. It would obviously be meaningless to regard social class as a ratio variable. One implication of such an assumption would be that SCII (code 2) × SCIII non-manual (code 3) = SCV (code 6) which is nonsense.

---

2   Tabulation

2.1   The *array* of data in Table 1 shows the age last birthday of 30 undergraduates entering university. If you were asked to discuss these data, what sorts of conclusions would you draw? How do you think that the data could be summarized, simply and clearly?

array

Table 1   Age last birthday of 30 undergraduates entering university

22	17	20	20	19
24	19	28	18	19
19	32	18	22	20
18	18	21	19	19
23	18	20	18	21
18	20	19	20	19

Spend a couple of minutes studying the data in Table 1 and summarize your conclusions in this space, then read paragraph 2.2 below.

Aged between 17 – 32, May i 18–21 range. Could give number i each range. Give average age of entry – either arithmetic or mode.

2.2 It is always difficult to make much sense of an array of data, even when there are only 30 observations. About all one can say of Table 1 is that most ages seem to be around 19 or 20, with one or two students being rather older. This is hardly a precise enough analysis, and the data obviously need to be summarized. The simplest method is to construct a table in which the variable is divided into a number of categories and the number of observations in each category is counted. Such a table, derived from measures on one variable, is known as a *univariate frequency distribution*. Thus in Table 2 the different ages in the array of data are listed, together with their *frequency*, i.e. the number of times they occur. The symbol f is usually used to denote frequency, and f_i is the frequency in the ith category, for example f_{20} is equal to 6 and $f_{25} = 0$.

univariate frequency distribution, frequency (f)

Table 2   Frequency distribution of ages in Table 1

Age last birthday (in years)	Number or frequency f_i
17	1
18	7
19	8
20	6
21	2
22	2
23	1
24	1
25	0
26	0
27	0
28	1
29	0
30	0
31	0
32	1
Total	30

SAQ 2
From the data set construct a frequency distribution for the variable 'number of children in household'.

2.3 As can be seen, the *frequency distribution* is a very helpful way of summarizing data, for it is now much easier to perceive the pattern or structure of ages. In practice we often find that this procedure is taken a step further in order to improve the presentation. The initial categories can be collapsed or grouped together to form a *grouped frequency distribution*. Table 3 shows one way in which this can be carried out for the ages of undergraduate entrants. Notice that

frequency distribution

grouped frequency distribution

the categories with the largest frequencies have been retained, that two others have been combined and that both end categories have been left 'open'. The table is now more compact and readable, and retains all the most important features of Table 2.

Table 3   Grouped frequency distribution of ages in Table 1

Age last birthday (in years)	Number or frequency f_i
Under 18	1
18	7
19	8
20	6
21–22	4
23–24	2
Over 24	2
Total	30

SAQ 3

From the data set, construct a grouped frequency distribution for the children's ability scores. You might take intervals of 20 marks starting with '0 but under 20', '20 but under 40', and so on.

2.4   The following points need to be borne in mind in constructing frequency distributions. To begin with, the categories should be *mutually exclusive,* in other words they should be constructed in such a way that each observation can be placed in one and only one category. Also the categories should be *exhaustive* in that all observations can be placed in one or other of the categories. Next, it must be remembered that a grouped frequency distribution always involves a loss of information compared with the *raw data;* but this is the price to be paid for conciseness. Thus, Table 3 contains the information that four entrants were aged 21 or 22 but we do not, from the table, know their exact ages; two entrants were aged 'over 24' but we do not know that their ages were in fact 28 and 32. In practice, whether loss of information is important depends on the questions one is asking of the data. If we were only interested in the age of mature students, then we could have combined all ages under 21 and kept all other observations in single age groups or the grouped categories shown in Table 3. On the other hand, a table such as Table 4 would be useless from almost any point of view as the information it conveys is almost negligible.

mutually exclusive

exhaustive

raw data

Table 4   Alternative grouped frequency distribution of ages in Table 1

Age last birthday (in years)	Number or frequency f_i
Under 18	1
18–31	28
32 and over	1
Total	30

2.5   So far we have only looked at frequency distributions for a variable measured on an interval scale, viz. age. Similar considerations apply to variables measured on other scales. Table 5 below is taken from Appendix 3 of the Plowden Report and shows the employment position of mothers in fatherless families and in families where both parents are present.

Table 5 Employment position of mothers in fatherless families and in families where both parents are present

Employment position of mother	Fatherless families	Both parents in family
Not working (away from home)	56	1 764
Away from home under 5 hours per day	12	512
Away from home 5 or more hours per day	53	455
Totals	121	2 731

Source: Plowden Report, Appendix 3

SAQ 4

In the Plowden Report, the full range of categories for the variable 'employment position of mother' shown in Table 5 was as follows:

Not gainfully employed	1
Hours irregular	2
Works on home premises	3
Away under 5 hours per day	4
Away 5 but less than 10 hours per day	5
Away 10 but less than 12 hours per day	6
Away 12 hours or over per day	7

To which scale of measurement does this variable correspond?

SAQ 5

What conclusions do you draw from Table 5?

2.6 The frequency distributions shown in Table 5 do permit a somewhat clearer summary of the employment position of the two groups of mothers than would have been possible using the raw ungrouped data. But there remains a difficulty in comparing the pattern of employment in the two groups which arises simply because the number of mothers in the two groups are so very different. In situations such as this it is best to standardize the data by constructing a *relative frequency distribution*. The procedure is simply to convert each frequency in a distribution into a percentage by dividing it by the base or total number and multiplying by 100, e.g. for mothers in fatherless families in Table 5, the 56 who are not working out of a total of 121 form $\frac{56}{121} \times 100 = 46\%$ of the total. This has been done in Table 6. Thus while in Table 5 it is difficult to compare the numbers 'not working' in the two groups, 56 and 1 764, in any sensible way, in Table 6 we see that these convert to 46% and 65% respectively. The percentages are directly comparable and show clearly the relative importance of the different employment categories within the two types of families.

relative frequency distribution

Table 6 Relative frequency distribution of the employment position of mothers in fatherless families and in families where both parents are present

Employment position of mother	Fatherless families %	Both parents in family %
Not working	46	65
Away from home under 5 hours per day	10	19
Away from home 5 or more hours per day	44	16
Total (%)	100	100
Total (numbers)	(121)	(2 731)

SAQ 6
What conclusions do you draw from Table 6?

2.7 It is sometimes useful to present the data in a frequency distribution for interval data in the form of a *cumulative frequency distribution,* which shows the number of *observations* that are less than (or greater than) a particular value. Table 7(a) shows the frequency distribution of net income of fathers in the 1964 Plowden National Survey and Table 7(b), the corresponding cumulative frequency distribution. There are 62 fathers with incomes of £7.50 or less, 196 with incomes of £10 or less and so on. Notice that we could have cumulated the numbers in the opposite direction – by calculating those with incomes of £30 and over, £25 and over, etc. In addition notice that we can cumulate (upwards or downwards) with a relative frequency distribution to produce a *cumulative relative frequency distribution* showing the percentage of fathers with over (or under) a given income.

margin: **cumulative frequency distribution, observation**

margin: **cumulative relative frequency distribution**

Table 7   Net incomes of fathers with children in primary school, 1964

(a) Frequency distribution		(b) Cumulative frequency distribution	
Net income (£ per week)	f	Net income (£ per week)	Cumulative frequency
Less than £7.50	62	Less than £7.50	62
£7.50 but less than £10	134	Less than £10	196
£10 but less than £12.50	386	Less than £12.50	582
£12.50 but less than £15	685	Less than £15	1 267
£15 but less than £20	908	Less than £20	2 175
£20 but less than £25	401	Less than £25	2 576
£25 but less than £30	157	Less than £30	2 733
£30 and over	155	All	2 888
Total	2 888		

Source: Plowden Report, Appendix 3

SAQ 7
Construct a cumulative frequency distribution and a cumulative relative frequency distribution for *either* (a) the number of children in household *or* (b) child's ability score.

Use the answers to SAQs 2 or 3 as a starting-point.

3   Graphic Representation

3.1 *Graphs* and *diagrams* can be used to represent clearly and visually the essential features of a frequency distribution. There are many alternative methods available, but only three – the bar-chart, the histogram and the ogive – will be considered here.

margin: **graph, diagram**

The Bar-chart

3.2 The *bar-chart* is a type of diagram which is appropriate for data measured on a nominal scale. The data in Table 8 show the type of secondary school which children in their last year in junior schools in the 1964 National Survey were

margin: **bar-chart**

going to attend the next year. The corresponding bar-chart for these data is shown in Figure 1. The procedure is to raise bars or blocks of equal width, corresponding

Table 8   Type of secondary school children in their last year in junior schools were going to attend

Type of secondary school	Number of children f_i
Grammar	235
Secondary Modern	624
Other	102
Not known	62
Total	1 023

Source: Plowden Report, Appendix 3

to each category in the table and to make the height of the blocks proportional to the frequencies in each category. In this case a scale of 1 cm for every 100 children has been used. Thus, the block for Grammar schools is 2.35 cm high, that for Secondary Modern schools 6.24 cm high and so on. The whole point is that the varying heights convey an impression of the relative importance of the four categories. Thus it can be seen at a glance that many more pupils will go to a Secondary Modern school than any other.

Figure 1   Bar-chart of data in Table 8

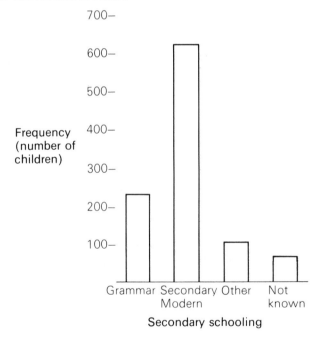

3.3   The characteristic of a nominal scale is that categories are simply separate and distinct with no implication of order or preference. This is reflected in the bar-chart, in that there is no scale on the horizontal axis. The bars can be of any convenient width, and can be placed in any convenient order; they are kept separate simply to emphasize the discrete nature of the categories.

SAQ 8
Use the data set to construct a frequency distribution and a bar-chart for the variable 'child's career'.

3.4 In the last section we saw the importance of comparing frequency distributions. Such comparisons can be made graphically by an adaptation of the bar-chart. For example, the secondary schools which children in junior schools were going to attend the next year, can be compared with the secondary schools which their parents hoped they would be attending. Table 9 shows the relevant relative frequency distributions and Figure 2 shows one way of comparing them

Table 9   Children in last year of juniors by actual and desired secondary schooling

Type of secondary school	Child was going to attend %	Parents wished their child to attend %
Grammar	23	51
Secondary Modern	61	24
Other	10	12
Not known	6	13
Total (%)	100	100
Total (numbers)	1 023	1 023

Source: Plowden Report, Appendix 3

diagramatically. Here, two bars of equal width and the same height are raised, representing the two relative frequency distributions. The height of each bar is divided in proportion to the relative frequencies representing each category. Thus for the type of secondary school the pupil was going to enter, 23% of the height is apportioned to Grammar schools, 61% to Secondary Modern, 10% to Other and 6% to Not known; a similar procedure is carried out for the second block. This presentation gives a clear visual illustration of the difference between parents' expectations of type of secondary school for their child and the actual school the child would in fact attend.

Figure 2   Bar-chart of data in Table 9

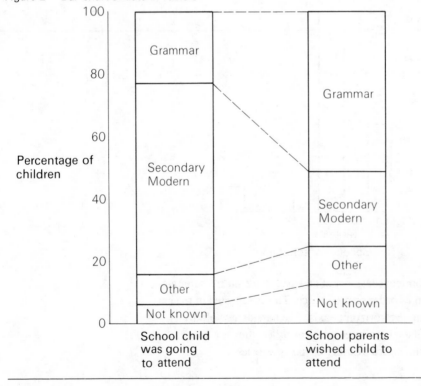

SAQ 9

Use the data set to construct a table similar to Table 9 to show the relative frequency distributions for attitude of parents to part-time jobs for boys and, separately, for girls. Use these distributions to construct a pair of bar-charts as in Figure 2.

The Histogram

3.5 A frequency distribution of data measured on an interval or ratio scale can be treated in an analogous way. Blocks can be raised over each interval or category of the distribution. But, unlike the bar-chart, the width of each block is made proportional to the size of the interval; the blocks are placed, in order, next to each other and since the width of *class intervals* may vary, the height of each block is adjusted until the *area* is proportional to the relative frequency. Such a diagram is known as a *histogram*.

class interval

histogram

3.6 The data in Table 10 show the frequency distribution of the household income of families in the 1964 National Survey (they have been slightly simplified for ease of computation). As can be seen, some intervals such as '£25 but under £30' are twice as large as others such as '£10 but under £12.50'. In raising a block over each of the intervals in the table the area of the block has to be made proportional to the frequency; the area of the block is equal to the base (or interval) multiplied by the height. Thus:

frequency $\propto$ area = height of block x width of interval

(*Note* The symbol '$\propto$' should be read as 'is proportional to'.)
The frequency and the width of intervals are known, and to obtain the relative heights we have to re-order the above so that:

height of block $\propto$ frequency $\div$ width of interval.

In other words, the height of each block is proportional to the relative frequency of observation in each measured interval of the variable, divided by the width of the interval. Thus column (iii) in Table 10 shows the width of each class interval and column (iv) shows the relative height. The effect of this operation can be seen by comparing the intervals '£10 but under £12.50' and '£25 but under £30'. The relative frequency is the same, 10% for each interval, but as the former interval is half as wide as the latter the block raised over the former has to be twice the height of the latter in order to make the areas of the block equal (see Figure 3).

3.7 The only remaining problem is the *open-ended group*, for incomes £30 and over. Here we have to make some assumption about the size of interval to be used and, purely for convenience, it is taken to be £10. The histogram for Table 10 is shown in Figure 3. Notice that the scale is represented by an area and not by a single vertical axis as in a bar-chart. The number on top of each block shows the frequency or relative frequency which the block represents.

open-ended group

Table 10   Frequency distribution of household income

Household income (£ per week)	Relative frequency %	Width of class interval	Relative frequency[2] Interval
(i)	(ii)	(iii)	$(iv) = \dfrac{(ii)}{(iii)}$
£7.50 but under £10	5	2.5	2
£10 but under £12.50	10	2.5	4
£12.50 but under £15	15	2.5	6
£15 but under £20	35	5	7
£20 but unter £25	20	5	4
£25 but under £30	10	5	2
£30 and over	5	10[1]	$\frac{1}{2}$
Total (%)	100		
Total (numbers)	2 888		

Source: Plowden Report, Appendix 3

Notes   [1] Arbitrary width of £10 chosen for final open class
[2] Column (iv) shows the frequency divided by the width of class interval and is proportional to the relative height of each block in the histogram

Figure 3   Histogram of data in Table 10

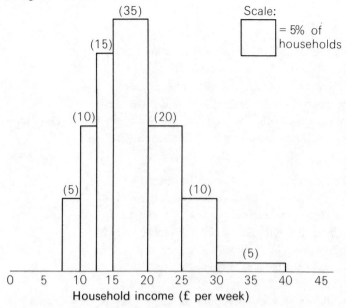

Note The figures in parentheses above each block correspond to the relative frequencies represented by the block

---

SAQ 10

Use the data set to construct a relative frequency distribution for family income. There are many ways of grouping the data. You should use the same intervals as those in Table 10, but introduce an additional interval of '£30 but under £40', so the final open-ended interval reads '£40 and over'.
Construct the relative frequency distribution, and then follow the workings in Table 10 to construct a histogram for family income.

3.8   Figure 3 is an example of a histogram where the frequency of observations in each interval is proportional to the area of the block. What then would have happened if, in this example, we had made (as with bar-charts) the heights proportional to the frequency? The result, using the same scale for the base, is shown in Figure 4 and, as can be seen, gives a very distorted visual impression of the distribution of households by income, with seemingly many more having high incomes than is actually the case. The reason is that we have ignored the fact that the 10% of households in intervals £10–£12.50, is spread only over a £2.50 range of income but that this 10% in the £25–£30 interval is spread over a £5 range of income, i.e. they are spread much more thinly. Essentially, we have ignored the fact that we need to look not at the frequency in each interval but at the rate of occurrence or the frequency per £ income.

Figure 4   Diagram of data in Table 10, with height proportional to frequency: a diagram of an incorrect histogram

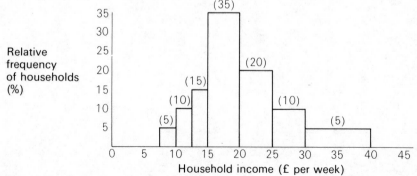

Note The figures in parentheses above each block correspond to the relative frequencies represented by the block

SAQ 11

If all the intervals in a grouped frequency distribution are the same size, can one make the heights of the blocks proportional to the frequencies?

Construct a relative frequency distribution and histogram for family income from the data set. Make all the intervals the same size, viz. £5. Thus you will have '£0 but under £5', '£5 but under £10', '£10 but under £15', and so on.

The Ogive

3.9 The final diagram to be considered is the graphic representation of a cumulative distribution which is known as an *ogive*. Remember that a cumulative distribution showed the numbers, or the percentages of observations falling below (or above) a given value (see paragraph 2.7). The cumulative frequency distribution and the relative cumulative frequency distribution for the data in Table 10 are given in Table 11. In Figure 5 the incomes of households are marked off along the *horizontal axis* and the cumulative and relative cumulative frequencies are marked off on the *vertical axis*. For convenience the upper limit of the open-ended group has again been taken to be £40. The ogive shown in Figure 5 is obtained by using straight lines to join up the points corresponding to the cumulative relative frequency at each income level. It is now relatively easy to read off the numbers and percentages of households with an income falling below a given value. Thus, for example, approximately 97% have an income less than £35.

ogive

see para. 2.7

horizontal axis, vertical axis

Table 11   Cumulative distributions of household income (data from Table 10)

Household income (£ per week)	Cumulative frequency	Relative cumulative frequency %
Less than £10	144	5
Less than £12.50	433	15
Less than £15	866	30
Less than £20	1 877	65
Less than £25	2 455	85
Less than £30	2 744	95
Less than £40	2 888	100

Source: Plowden Report, Appendix 3

Figure 5   Ogive presenting the data in Table 11

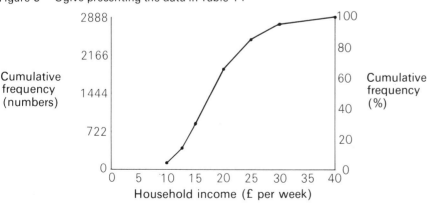

SAQ 12

Take the relative frequency distribution for family income which was found in SAQ 11 and find the cumulative relative frequency distribution. Construct an ogive, as in Figure 5, to represent the data.

4 Measures of Location or Central Tendency

4.1 We have seen in the last two sections that raw data can usefully be summarized by constructing frequency distributions and graphs of various kinds. But it is often beneficial and necessary to summarize to an even greater degree by calculating a single quantity or *statistic* which conveys one of the essential features of the distribution. Look at Figure 6 below. It shows the *idealized* age distributions of individuals working in two different occupations. These distributions have been called idealized because they have been represented in Figure 6 by smooth curves. In practice the age distribution of a *population* or *sample* of individuals will have the usual stepped appearance of a histogram. The curves shown in Figure 6 are intended to convey the typical shape of the histograms of such age distributions. Both distributions are roughly the same shape, but, on the whole, Group II is older than Group I.

statistic, idealize

population, sample

4.2 A useful way of summarizing the two distributions, would be to find a typical or *central measure* for each group which would bring out the fact that, on the whole, members of Group II are located higher up the age scale than those in Group I. In layman's terms what we require is the '*average*' of each group or, in statistical terms, *a measure of location or central tendency* for each distribution. The term 'average' is however rather unclear. It is a single concept but there are many different kinds of 'average' or measures of location, each making different assumptions about the data, calculated in different ways and for different purposes. We shall look at three measures of location – the mode, the median and the mean – and we shall see that each of these measures can be calculated for a set of data measured on an interval or ratio scale. But a mean cannot be calculated for data measured on an ordinal or nominal scale, nor can a median be calculated for nominal data. Only the mode can be used as a measure of location for all measurement scales, but in using a mode to summarize ordinal and interval data or in using a median to summarize interval data some information may be lost. These remarks should be borne in mind as you read on and work through the remainder of this section and you should find that they become clearer. All the examples which follow are based upon interval or ratio scale data.

central measure

measure of location or central tendency

Figure 6 Age distribution of men in two occupations

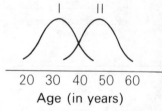

The Mode

4.3 The *mode* is the simplest type of average or measure of location. It is the 'most common' value or category of a variable; in other words the value that occurs most often in a frequency distribution. For example, the following set of data:

$$3\ 4\ 5\ 5\ 5\ 6\ 6\ 7\ 8$$

has this frequency distribution:

Value	f_i	
3	1	
4	1	
5	3	← mode
6	2	
7	1	
8	1	

mode

Here the mode or *modal value* for the distribution is 5 because this value occurs most frequently. Thus, mode = 5.

modal value

4.4 The mode has the advantage of being relatively easy to find, providing there is only one modal value for a particular distribution, but if two or more values of the variable occur with the same maximum frequency, then the distribution is bi-modal or multi-modal and the mode is then less useful or meaningful as a summary measure. If all values of the variable occur with equal frequency, then the mode cannot be said to exist at all for such a distribution. Where there is a unique mode for a frequency distribution, then a bar-chart or histogram will have a peak corresponding to the modal value of the variable. A *modal category* can usually be found for a set of categories of a variable classified on a nominal scale, indeed the mode is the only form of 'average' for a nominal variable with several categories. In practice, the mode is rarely used in social science research because it is generally less useful than the median and mean.

bi-modal distribution, multi-modal distribution

modal category

4.5   However, a *dichotomous variable* (a nominal variable with only two categories) can be summarized meaningfully in a rather different way. For such a variable the proportion of observations in the data set which fall in one (or other) of the two categories represents a very meaningful summary of the data and it is possible to interpret this proportion as a form of average analogous to the mean. This will be discussed more fully in paragraphs 4.34 and 4.35 below, after consideration of the median and mean and comparison of the three summary measures.

dichotomous variable

see paras 4.34 and 4.35

SAQ 13
Use the data set to find the mode for the four variables:
(a)   Occupation of father
(b)   Number of children in household
(c)   Attitude of parents to part-time job
(d)   Career.

The Median

4.6   The *median* is a measure of location requiring a rather more stringent set of assumptions than the mode, since it assumes that the values or categories of the variable can be ranked. It is defined as that value of the variable which, if the observations are placed in rank order, will divide the overall distribution into two halves such that exactly half of the observations in the data set will be below the median value and half will be above it.

median

4.7   Suppose you have the following set of observations:

$$8 \ 4 \ 6 \ 10 \ 2 \ 12$$

When these are ranked in order from lowest value to highest we get:

$$2 \ 4 \ 6 \downarrow 8 \ 10 \ 12$$

With an even number of observations, as we have here, the median value will lie between the third observation and the fourth, such that there are three observations smaller, and three larger than it. By convention, it is taken to be halfway between the two central values, i.e. between 6 and 8. Thus the median in this case is:

$$\tilde{X} = 7$$

If there are an odd number of observations, e.g.

$$2 \ 4 \ 6 \ 8 \ 10$$
$$\downarrow$$

then the median is just that value of the variable corresponding to the *central observation*; in this example the value of the third observation, so that:

central observation

$$\tilde{X} = 6$$

4.8   In these two examples the median would have had the same value if the observations had been arranged in decreasing rather than increasing order of value. Thus the median of the following set of observations,

$$10 \quad 8 \quad 6 \quad 4 \quad 2$$
$$\downarrow$$

remains as $\tilde{X} = 6$. It should be obvious to you that this will be true of the distribution of values in any data set.

4.9   In general, the location of the median in an ordered array of data is the value of the $\left(\dfrac{n + 1}{2}\right)^{\text{th}}$ observation, where n is the total number of observations. In the first example above, $n = 6$ so that the median is the value of the $\left(\dfrac{6 + 1}{2}\right)^{\text{th}} = 3\frac{1}{2}^{\text{th}}$ observation, which of course, does not exist, so the median is taken to be the value lying mid-way between the third and fourth observations. In the second, $n = 5$ and the median is the value of the $\left(\dfrac{5 + 1}{2}\right)^{\text{th}} = 3\text{rd}$ observation.

SAQ 14
Use the data set to find the median family income for the first eight cases in the data set.

4.10   The same procedure can be used if data are presented in the form of an ungrouped frequency distribution. In Table 12 below we have the marks out of a total of 5, gained by 19 candidates in a history examination. In this case it helps to construct a cumulative frequency distribution showing that two candidates scored 0 marks, five scored 1 or less, eleven scored 2 or less and so on. With $n = 19$ the median value is the score of the $\left(\dfrac{n + 1}{2}\right)^{\text{th}} = \left(\dfrac{19 + 1}{2}\right)^{\text{th}} = 10\text{th person}$. The tenth person obtained a score of 2, so the median history score for these 19 candidates is $\tilde{X} = 2$.

Table 12   Marks in a history examination

Marks	Frequency	Cumulative frequency
0	2	2
1	3	5
2	6	11
3	4	15
4	3	18
5	1	19
Total	19	

SAQ 15
Find the median for the variable 'number of children in household'. Use the ungrouped frequency distribution which was found in the answer to SAQ 2.

4.11 The median is a useful measure of location which, because it is based upon a ranking of the data, retains more of the information contained in the data than does the mode. But the point to notice is that although it uses the idea of ranking and rank order it does not take into account the overall distribution of values. For the four sets of data shown below, the patterns of the distribution are quite different:

(a) 10 10 10 10   10
(b)   8   9 10 11   12
(c)   0   1 10 11   12
(d)   8   9 10 50 100

In set (a) all the values are the same: there is no variation about a central value; in set (b) the values are distributed symmetrically about a central value; in set (c) there are two relatively low values, and in (d) two relatively high values. In each case, however, the median is the same, $\tilde{X} = 10$, for it is simply the middle value in rank order. The median does not take into account how large or small are the values on either side, nor on the distribution of values overall; it is simply concerned with the *number* of observations on either side.

4.12 By definition a median value can only exist for a data set in which the values can be placed in rank order, so it is not possible to find a median for nominal data. Clearly a median value can always be found for ordinal, interval or ratio data. Open University grades A, B, C, D, E and F constitute an ordinal scale, so it is always possible to find the median grade for any group of students. Finally, note that the median is one example of a *'positional' measure*, locating as it does the position of a given observation *relative* to the remaining observations in a data set.

positional measure

The Arithmetic Mean

4.13 The most important measure of location for the distribution of a variable measured on an interval or ratio scale is the *arithmetic mean,* which is often referred to simply as the *mean*. It takes every value in a distribution directly into account, and involves arithmetical operations on the values. It is for this reason that it should be calculated only for interval or ratio scale data. The mean is defined as *the sum of the values of all the observations in the data set divided by the number of observations in the set.* The mean can be thought of as a 'typical' value of the data set. Suppose a given data set represents the incomes of a number of individuals, then the mean is that income each would have if the total income were shared out so that they all had the same income.

arithmetic mean

4.14 For the following set of values,

$$8 \quad 10 \quad 12 \quad 14 \quad 16$$

$$\text{the arithmetic mean} = \frac{\text{Sum of values}}{\text{Number of observations}}$$

Since the sum of values is $8 + 10 + 12 + 14 + 16 = 60$ and the number of observation is 5, then

$$\text{the arithmetic mean} = \frac{60}{5} = 12$$

4.15 The arithmetic mean is usually written in symbolic notation. If there are n observations of a variable labelled X_i, where X_1 is the value of the first observation, X_2, the second and X_n the last, then the sum of the values is written as:

$$X_1 + X_2 + \ldots\ldots + X_n = \sum_{i=1}^{n} X_i$$

where Σ (the Greek letter capital sigma) stands for 'the sum of'. The expression on the right-hand side of the equation thus states the sum must be taken of all values X_i from $i = 1$ (i.e. X_1) through to $i = n$ (i.e. X_n), known as the limits of summation.

4.16   If the arithmetic mean is denoted by $\bar{X}$ (read 'X bar') then:

$$\bar{X} = \frac{\text{Sum of values}}{\text{Number of observations}} = \frac{\sum_{i=1}^{n} X_i}{n}$$

or,

$$= \frac{1}{n} \sum_{i=1}^{n} X_i$$

For simplicity, the limits of the summation sign will be dropped for the remainder of this unit and the arithmetic mean will be written as:

$$\bar{X} = \frac{1}{n} \Sigma X_i$$

but in any such expression it is understood that the summation extends over all observations in the data set from X_1 to X_n unless stated otherwise.

4.17   We can now rewrite the above example in terms of these symbols such that:

$$X_1 = 8$$
$$X_2 = 10$$
$$X_3 = 12$$
$$X_4 = 14$$
$$X_5 = 16$$

Thus, the number of observations is $n = 5$ and the sum of values is

$$\Sigma X_i = (X_1 + X_2 + X_3 + X_4 + X_5)$$
$$= (8 + 10 + 12 + 14 + 16)$$
$$= 60$$

The arithmetic mean is:

$$\bar{X} = \frac{1}{n} \Sigma X_i = \frac{1}{5} \times 60$$
$$= 12$$

This symbolic notation might not seem to be very useful where the data set contains only a few observations, but the simple expression,

$$\bar{X} = \frac{\Sigma X_i}{n}$$

summarizes the definition of the arithmetic mean for any data set, even those containing thousands of observations, and this notation provides a very convenient shorthand.

SAQ 16

Use the data set to find the arithmetic mean for the variables:
(a)   Family income
(b)   Child's ability score.
Use only the first 10 cases in the data set.

4.18   If the data are in the form of a frequency distribution, the concept of the mean of the distribution is unchanged, but the method of calculation changes slightly. Table 13 shows the distribution of the number of children in 20 households. To calculate the mean number of children per household we need to find the total number of children. This can be done in two stages, by first finding the total number of children in each category and then adding these category totals. With 'X_i' referring to the number of children and f_i to the number of families, column (iii) of Table 13 shows two households with no children, i.e. category total of 0; four households with 1 child, a category total of 4; and so on.

Table 13   Number of children in 20 households

X_i (i)	f_i (ii)	$f_i X_i$ (iii) = (ii) × (i)
0	2	0
1	4	4
2	8	16
3	4	12
4	2	8
Total	$n = 20$	$\Sigma f_i X_i = 40$

The arithmetic mean $= \dfrac{\text{Total number of children}}{\text{Total number of families}}$

This is given by:

$$\bar{X} = \frac{1}{n} \Sigma f_i X_i = \frac{40}{20}$$

$$= 2 \text{ children per household}$$

4.19   You could check that the median number of children per family for these 20 families is 2, the same as the mean. The modal value is also 2 children per family since eight families have this number of children. So, for this distribution mean, median and mode all have the same value. This is always true for a *symmetrical distribution* which the present one is. As you can see, the 20 families are distributed symmetrically about the central value of 2 children per family. A histogram of this distribution illustrates the symmetry graphically (see Figure 7).

symmetrical distribution

Figure 7

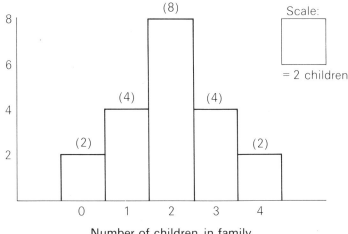

Number of children in family

SAQ 17
Find the arithmetic mean of the number of children in household for the whole data set. Use the frequency distribution which was found in the answer to SAQ 2 and follow the workings in Table 13.

4.20   The most important point to grasp about the mean is that it involves a consideration of all the values in a distribution. It is analogous to the idea of *centre of gravity* in physics. If we have two equal weights at either end of a plank, then the point of balance, or centre of gravity, will be in the centre of the plank, as illustrated in Figure 8.

centre of gravity

Figure 8

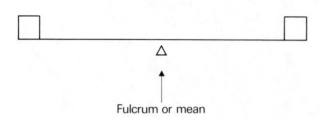

Fulcrum or mean

If, however, a third weight is placed at one end, then the centre of gravity has to move towards the 'heavier' end, as shown in Figure 9.

Figure 9

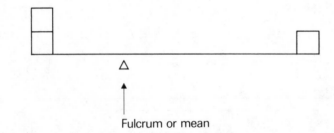

Fulcrum or mean

4.21   The arithmetic mean of a frequency distribution is like a *fulcrum*, with the 'weights' being equivalent to the frequency, and the distribution along the plank being equivalent to the values; so that for two values 2 and 8, the mean is in the centre, $\bar{X} = 5$, but for three values 2, 2 and 8, the mean moves towards the value occurring more often and $\bar{X} = 4$.

4.22   The fact that all values of a distribution are taken into account in calculating the mean has important consequences, for, unlike the median, extremely large (or small) values, compared with the main body of values, will have a strong influence on the mean. In example (a) below, the mean of $\bar{X} = 4$ is 'representative' or typical of the distribution. But this is not so in (b) where the one large value, 106, has dragged the mean upwards to $\bar{X} = 24$.

(a)   2 3 4 5 6 $\bar{X} = \dfrac{20}{5} = 4$

(b)   2 3 4 5 106 $\bar{X} = \dfrac{120}{5} = 24$

Considerations of this kind must influence when and how the mean is used in practice as a descriptive statistic.

4.23   There are two further characteristics of the mean which are important. Firstly, if the mean of a distribution is subtracted from each value of the distribution, then a set of differences or *deviations* from the mean is obtained; the sum of these deviations is always zero. As an example we can take the data in Table 14. We first calculate the arithmetic mean and find that $\bar{X} = 7$. The mean is

deviation

now subtracted from each value of X_i as is shown in column (ii), so that for $X_i = 2$, $(X_i - \overline{X}) = -5$, for $X_i = 4$, $(X_i - \overline{X}) = -3$, and so on. As you can see some of the resulting differences are positive and some negative and if they are summed, i.e. $\Sigma(X_i - \overline{X})$ then the total is zero. This is always the case for any set of numbers or any frequency distribution.

Table 14   Differences from the mean

X (i)	$(X_i - \overline{X})$ (ii)
2	-5
4	-3
6	-1
8	$+1$
10	$+3$
12	$+5$
$\Sigma(X_i - \overline{X}) = 0$	

SAQ 18

Show that the sum of the differences between each value and the mean value is zero for the first ten cases of each variable 'family income' and 'child's ability score'. The arithmetic mean of each was found in the answer to SAQ 16.

4.24 The second important and very useful characteristic of the arithmetic mean is that, given the value of the mean and the number of observations, we can always find the sum of the values, i.e.

$$\Sigma X = n\overline{X}$$

Thus, if we know that the mean age of five children is 8 years, i.e.

$$n = 5$$

and

$$\overline{X} = 8 \text{ years}$$

then we can find the total ages of the children by calculation:

$$\Sigma X = n\overline{X} = (5)(8) = 40 \text{ years}$$

A consequence of this is that if we know $\overline{X}$ and n for each of two groups of children, then we can easily find the overall mean for the two groups combined. Thus if we have two groups with means $\overline{X}_1$ and $\overline{X}_2$ respectively and numbers of observations n_1 and n_2 respectively, then the mean $\overline{X}$ of the *combined groups* is given as:

$$\overline{X} = \frac{n_1\overline{X}_1 + n_2\overline{X}_2}{n_1 + n_2}$$

4.25 For example, with two groups of 5 children, whose average ages are $\overline{X}_1 = 8$ and $\overline{X}_2 = 12$, then the average age of the 10 children together is:

$$\overline{X} = \frac{(5)(8) + (5)(12)}{5 + 5} = \frac{40 + 60}{10} = \frac{100}{10} = 10 \text{ years}$$

In this respect, the mean has a distinct advantage over the median for there is no way of finding the combined median of two groups of values without having all values of the combined data set available.

SAQ 19

For the first ten cases in the data set, find (a) the arithmetic mean of the ability score for boys, and (b) the arithmetic mean of the ability score for girls. Using the formula in paragraph 4.24 above find (c) the arithmetic mean score for boys and girls together.

Comparison of Mean, Median and Mode

4.26 Usually only one measure of location is used in analysing the distribution of a variable. The selection of which one to use in any particular context is partly a matter of judgement based on a knowledge of the characteristics of the statistic and the research question in hand.

4.27 Fundamentally, the use of a particular 'average' is determined by the scale of measurement which can be assumed for the data. The position is summarized in Table 15 below. For data on a nominal scale, there is no choice, the mode is the only appropriate measure. For ordinal scale data a choice is available and either the median or the mode may be appropriate, but the median is preferable for the reasons given in paragraph 4.11 above; it retains more of the information contained in the data set by taking into account the rank order of the values.

4.28 However, the median conveys very little useful information where the data represent a set of individual rankings without numerical scores associated with the ranks. To know that in a race, the median person is the 5th to finish, says little except that, in all, nine people finished the race. On the other hand, when there are ranked groups, the median is more useful, as it now may be useful to separate the cases into one of two categories according to whether they are above or below the median. If exam results are graded A, B, C, D, E and F and the median group is E, this does convey some useful, though not very precise, information about the distribution of scores in that as many candidates failed as gained passes higher than E. As data measured on interval or ratio scales, any of the measures may be used and the comparative merits of the mean and the median then become important.

Table 15   Measures of location that may be used with given scales of measurement

	Mode	Median	Mean
Nominal	Yes	No	No
Ordinal	Yes	Yes	No
Interval/ratio	Yes	Yes	Yes

4.29 The choice between the mean and the median as a measure of location for interval or ratio scale data depends very much on the shape of the distribution. The median as was shown earlier is not affected by 'extreme' values as it only takes into account the *rank order* of observations. The mean on the other hand *is* affected by extremely large or small values as it specifically takes the *values* of the observations into account, not just their rank order. Thus in (a) below the mean equals the median and $\bar{X} = \tilde{X} = 6$. But in (b), which is the same distribution except for one extremely large value, the median remains as $\tilde{X} = 6$ but the mean increases substantially to $\bar{X} = 20$:

(a) 2 4 6 8 10 $\tilde{X} = 6$ $\bar{X} = 6$
(b) 2 4 6 8 80 $\tilde{X} = 6$ $\bar{X} = 20$

4.30 If a distribution has a few 'extreme' scores, then these can exert a disproportionate effect on the mean; and if you are looking for a simple statistic representing a typical value in order to describe or summarize a distribution, then the mean can be a quite inappropriate measure. In (b) above it is a little difficult to consider $\bar{X} = 20$ as being 'typical' of the distribution. In general, if a distribution is substantially skewed, that is, when the bulk of observations are clustered together but a few have much higher or much lower values, then the median is usually preferred to the mean.

4.31   As a descriptive statistic, a distribution is said to be *'symmetrical'* if mean, median and mode coincide and the shape of the distribution is identical on both sides of the central value. An idealized form of symmetrical distribution is shown in Figure 10 (a). If a distribution has a few very large values it is said to be *positively skewed*. The idealized form is shown in Figure 10 (b); this kind of distribution has a tail extending to the right with the mean greater than the median which is greater than the mode. If a distribution has a few very small values it is said to be *negatively skewed*; it has a tail extending to the left as in Figure 10 (c) and the mean is less than the median which is less than the mode.

symmetrical distribution

positive skewness

negative skewness

Figure 10   The relationship of the mode, median ($\tilde{X}$) and mean ($\bar{X}$)

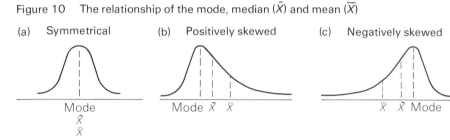

(a)   Symmetrical   (b)   Positively skewed   (c)   Negatively skewed

4.32   Thus, the mean is affected much more by skewness than is the median, and for skewed distributions the median is preferred. Distributions of income or earnings are usually positively skewed and the median is used to summarize and compare such distributions. However, there are many situations in the social sciences where the data are symmetrically distributed or only moderately skewed and then the mean can be used.

4.33   It is always best from an analytic viewpoint to use the mean whenever possible. The reasons for this will become clear in later Blocks, but very briefly they are, firstly, that many of the summary measures used in descriptive statistics can be and are used in more complex analyses which are included in Blocks 6 and 7, such as *multiple correlation, multiple regression,* etc. The development of all these more complex methods relies on mathematical analysis and the mean which is calculated arithmetically is mathematically much easier to manipulate than the median which is found by ordering. Secondly, much of the data used in research derives from samples and from *sampling procedures*. As will be seen in Block 3, any sampling procedure leads to *'sampling errors'* for a particular statistic, i.e. we can only estimate the mean or median income or age in a given population within certain *limits of error. Sampling theory* shows that this error or *'uncertainty'* is less for the mean than for the median. Thus for most purposes we find that the mean is used in preference to the median, except when the distributions are substantially skewed.

**multiple correlation,
multiple regression**

**sampling procedure,
sampling error**

**limits of error,
sampling theory,
uncertainty**

SAQ 20
Look at the following two histograms representing 'family income' and 'child's ability score'.

(a)   Are the distributions skewed and, if so, in what direction?

(b)   In each case, would you say that the mode and arithmetic mean are likely to be greater than, equal to or less than the median?

Figure 11   Histogram of 'family income' from 30 cases in data set

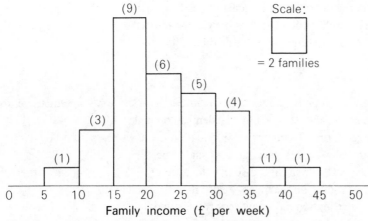

Family income (£ per week)

Note   The figures in parentheses above each block correspond to the relative frequencies represented by the block

Figure 12   Histogram of 'child's ability score' from 30 cases in data set

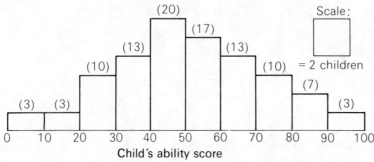

Child's ability score

Note   The figures in parentheses above each block correspond to the relative frequencies represented by the block

---

4.34   Description and analysis of dichotomous data usually proceed by considering the *proportion* of observations which fall in each category. Consider the data represented in Table 5 above, showing the employment position of mothers in fatherless families. The data can be grouped to form a dichotomous variable with two categories as follows:

proportion
see Table 5, para. 2.5

Category of variable	*Number of mothers or frequency*
Mother gainfully employed	65
Mother *not* gainfully employed	56
All mothers of fatherless families	121

These data can be summarized by one figure or statistic, the proportion of mothers gainfully employed. This is:

$$\frac{65}{121} = 0.54$$

The proportion of mothers in the other category, '*not* gainfully employed', must be the complement of this, i.e. 0.46.

4.35   This statistic could have been calculated in a different way. Suppose that the value '1' is allocated to the 'gainfully employed' category such that each mother gainfully employed 'scores' 1; and the value '0' is allocated to the 'not gainfully employed' category such that each mother not gainfully employed 'scores' 0, or zero. This variable, the employment status of mothers, is now known as a *dummy variable*; with only two possible scores it is assumed to be measured on an interval or ratio scale and as such the arithmetic mean can be found as shown in Table 16 below. The result is exactly the same as the proportion of mothers gainfully employed.

dummy variable

Table 16

Category	Score X_i	Frequency f_i	$f_i X_i$
Mother gainfully employed	1	65	65
Mother *not* gainfully employed	0	56	0
			$\Sigma f_i X_i = 65$

$$\overline{X} = \frac{1}{n}\Sigma f_i X_i = \frac{65}{121}$$

$$= 0.54$$

At first sight this procedure may seem unnecessarily complicated but it can be extremely useful and we shall come back to it again in paragraph 8.29 below. The analysis of dichotomous data is treated more fully in Block 6, Part 2 and the dummy variable technique is used again in Block 7, Part 1.

see para. 8.29

5   Measures of Dispersion

5.1   Averages or measures of location are a useful way of describing one characteristic of a frequency distribution. But reducing a large set of data to one statistic can lead to a serious loss of information. Consider the three distributions below. Both mean and median are equal for each distribution, i.e. $\overline{X} = \tilde{X} = 10$, but a second characteristic differs quite markedly in each:

(a)   8   9 10 11 12
(b)   10 10 10 10 10
(c)   1   5 10 15 19

Can you see how these three distributions differ? Summarize the differences briefly in this space, then read paragraph 5.2 below.

5.2 The major differences between the distributions is the degree to which the values are *dispersed* or vary around the mean or median. In (b) there is no *variation*, as all the values are equal; in (a) there is some variation as the values range from 8 to 12; and in (c) the variation is much larger with a spread of values from 1 to 19. Measures of location are obviously not designed to assess this second characteristic; *measures of dispersion or variation* are required.

dispersion, variation

measure of dispersion or variation

5.3 It is a truism to say that human behaviour and characteristics are inherently and infinitely variable. The identification of the variability of characteristics of individuals and groups, an assessment of its strength and the consequent search for explanations as to the reasons for such variation is at the heart of all social research. Thus the variation in unemployment rates between regions and local areas is usually of more interest than the crude national average; the dispersion or inequality in incomes may be a more fruitful research topic than a consideration of the average income; in a study of teaching methods the spread of abilities of children in a class is more relevant than the 'average' ability.

5.4 Consider the data on wages of five work sectors in a firm shown in Table 17 below. In each sector, the median wage is the same, $\tilde{X} = £45$. Given this fact alone, we might be tempted to conclude that the wage structure is the same in each sector. But a glance at the different distributions shows immediately that simply using an 'average' wage to compare the sectors has ignored the large differences in the variability or dispersion of wages and might well lead us to ignore important organizational differences between the sectors.

Table 17   Relative frequency distributions of weekly wages in five sectors of a firm

Weekly wage £	Sectors				
	I	II	III	IV	V
20 but less than 30	50	10	20	0	0
30 but less than 40	0	20	20	0	25
40 but less than 50	0	40	20	100	50
50 but less than 60	0	20	20	0	25
60 but less than 70	50	10	20	0	0
	100	100	100	100	100

5.5 Thus in general, the degree of variation or dispersion in a data set is as important and often more important than the average value. Just as we needed to seek measures of location to represent average value, we need measures of dispersion to represent variation. A number of different measures are available and the two most useful – the quartile deviation and the variance – will be described. These are two descriptive statistics which share a basic underlying conception that if there is no variation between values in a data set, then the resulting statistic has a value of zero, and as the variation gets larger or the values more 'spread out', then the value of the statistic gets larger.

The Quartile Deviation

5.6 The *quartile deviation* is a 'positional' measure, like the median, and similarly depends on the idea of ranks and ranked values or scores. The median, as we saw, was the value which divided a distribution into two halves, so that half the values fell below the median value and half above. There is no reason why this idea cannot be extended to any other position or rank. Thus we can find

quartile deviation (*QD*)

percentiles which will divide a distribution of ranked values into hundredths or 100 groups, or we can find *deciles* which will divide a distribution into tenths or 10 groups.

percentile, decile

5.7 For the quartile deviation, however, the distribution is divided into quarters, with Q_1 or the *lower quartile* being the value such that, if all the observations are ranked, a quarter of the observation.have a lower value, and three-quarters, a higher value; and Q_3 or the *upper quartile* being the value such that three quarters of the observations have a lower value, and a quarter, higher values. Then $Q_3 - Q_1$, known as the *inter-quartile range,* contains 50% of the observations, and the quartile deviation is defined as:

lower quartile (Q_1)

upper quartile (Q_3)

inter-quartile range

$$QD = \frac{Q_3 - Q_1}{2}$$

5.8 For the eight observations shown below, Q_1 lies halfway between the second and third observation and Q_3 halfway between the sixth and seventh observation:

$$2 \quad 4 \mid 6 \quad 8 \mid 10 \quad 12 \mid 14 \quad 16$$
$$\downarrow \qquad \downarrow \qquad \downarrow$$
$$Q_1 \qquad \bar{X} \qquad Q_3$$

Thus, with $Q_1 = 5$ and $Q_3 = 13$, the quartile deviation,

$$QD = \frac{13 - 5}{2} = 4$$

SAQ 21

Find the quartile deviation for 'family income' and for 'number of children in household' for the first eight cases in the data set.

5.9 The procedure for calculating quartiles Q_3 and Q_1 for a frequency distribution such as that shown in Table 13 is similar to calculating the median. Alternatively, quartiles can be easily derived from a graph of the cumulative distribution. For a unimodal distribution, i.e. one with a single peak, the relationship between Q_3, Q_1 and the median gives an idea of whether the distribution is skewed or not, and if it is, which way it is skewed: if $(Q_3 - \tilde{X}) = (\tilde{X} - Q_1)$ then the distribution is usually roughly symmetric; if $(Q_3 - \tilde{X}) > (\tilde{X} - Q_1)$ then the distribution is likely to be positively skewed; and if $(Q_3 - \tilde{X}) < (\tilde{X} - Q_1)$ then it is negatively skewed. The three possibilities are shown in Figure 13 below.

Figure 13 The relationship between skewness and quartiles

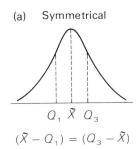 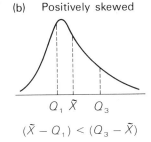 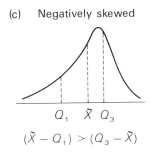

(a) Symmetrical   (b) Positively skewed   (c) Negatively skewed

$Q_1 \quad \tilde{X} \quad Q_3$ $Q_1 \quad \tilde{X} \quad Q_3$ $Q_1 \quad \tilde{X} \quad Q_3$

$(\tilde{X} - Q_1) = (Q_3 - \tilde{X})$ $(\tilde{X} - Q_1) < (Q_3 - \tilde{X})$ $(\tilde{X} - Q_1) > (Q_3 - \tilde{X})$

5.10 The quartile deviation is a useful measure of variation in the same circumstances, and for the same reasons, as the median is a useful measure of location, and they are invariably used in conjunction with one another.

The Variance and Standard Deviation

5.11   An alternative way of looking at the variation in a data set is to compare each value in a distribution with the mean. The larger the differences between the values and the mean are on average, the greater is the variation. Thus both the distributions (a) and (b) below have a mean of 10. If we calculate $(X_i - \bar{X})$ for each distribution then the differences are generally larger in (b) than in (a); the largest difference in (a) is between 9 and 10, or between 11 and 10, i.e. -1 or $+1$ whilst the largest difference in (b) is between 1 and 10 or between 10 and 19, i.e. -9 or $+9$.

	Values (X_i)	Mean	Differences ($X_i - \bar{X}$)
(a)	9 10 10 10 11	$\bar{X} = 10$	-1 0 0 $0 + 1$
(b)	1 5 10 15 19	$\bar{X} = 10$	$-9 - 5$ $0 + 5 + 9$

5.12   The idea of difference or deviation from the mean is fundamental to the measure of variation called the 'variance'. It might seem at first sight that a useful measure of variation would be the sum of these differences, i.e. $\Sigma(X_i - \bar{X})$ but, as we saw earlier in paragraph 4.23 above, some differences are positive and some are negative; they always cancel each other out and the resulting sum is always zero.

5.13   The problem arises because of the 'sign' of the differences; some are negative and some are positive. Two methods can be used to 'get rid of' the sign: one way is simply to ignore them, the other way is to square them. The former solution – which is known as taking the *'absolute' differences* – does lead to an acceptable solution. We can sum the absolute differences and divide this by the number of differences (otherwise the result may depend on the *number* of values and not the variation in values). This statistic, the mean of the absolute deviations, is known as the *mean deviation* so that:

absolute difference

mean deviation

$$MD = \frac{1}{n} \Sigma |(X_i - \bar{X})|$$

where, in $|(X_i - \bar{X})|$, the vertical bars tell us to ignore the sign of the difference.

5.14   Thus for the data in Table 18 we first calculate the mean,

$$\bar{X} = \frac{1}{n} \Sigma X_i = \frac{30}{5}$$
$$= 6$$

Column (ii) then shows the difference from the mean for each value; column (iii) shows the absolute differences.

Table 18   Calculation of the Mean Deviation

X_i (i)	$(X_i - \bar{X})$ (ii)	$|(X_i - \bar{X})|$ (iii)
2	-4	4
4	-2	2
6	0	0
8	$+2$	2
10	$+4$	4
$\Sigma X_i = 30$	$\Sigma(X_i - \bar{X}) = 0$	$\Sigma|(X_i - \bar{X})| = 12$

Thus:

$$MD = \frac{1}{n} \Sigma(X_i - \bar{X}) = \frac{12}{5}$$
$$= 2.4$$

SAQ 22
Find the mean deviation of 'child's ability score' for the first ten cases in the data set. It will help if you look at the answers to SAQs 16 and 18.

5.15   This measure does 'work' in a practical sense in that for a distribution with no variation the mean deviation will have a value of zero, and the wider the variation in the data, the larger will be the value of the mean deviation. It is intuitively easy to understand and is a useful descriptive measure of dispersion. However, it is very rarely used simply because it leads to difficult and often intractable mathematical problems both for more complex statistical method and for drawing conclusions from samples of data taken from a larger population.

5.16   It is theoretically advantageous, and in practice much more convenient, to square the deviations from the mean, sum them and then divide the result by the number of observations. The mean of the sum of squared deviations is known as the *variance* and is usually given the symbol s^2. Thus:

variance (s^2)

$$s^2 = \frac{1}{n} \Sigma (X_i - \bar{X})^2$$

5.17   The variance is an important statistical measure in itself and you will come across it later in the course. As a descriptive statistic, however, it does have the disadvantage that in squaring the differences we also square the units involved, and have a measure involving, say £^{2} or (years of age)^2. To avoid this we derive the *standard deviation* which is simply the square root of the variance. Thus the standard deviation is:

standard deviation (s)

$$s = \sqrt{\frac{1}{n} \Sigma (X_i - \bar{X})^2}$$

Note: the Greek letter σ (lower case sigma) is used to represent the standard deviation of a population, but s is usually used for samples and for data sets.

5.18   An example of its calculation is shown in Table 19 for the same distribution used in the calculation of mean deviation in Table 18. Columns (i) and (ii) are identical to the corresponding columns in Table 18. This time, column (iii) shows the squares of the deviations from the mean rather than their absolute values as before. The value for the standard deviation in Table 19 is just slightly greater than the value obtained for the mean deviation in Table 18.

Table 19   Calculation of a standard deviation

X_i (i)	$(X_i - \bar{X})$ (ii)	$(X_i - \bar{X})^2$ (iii)
2	-4	16
4	-2	4
6	0	0
8	$+2$	4
10	$+4$	16
$\Sigma X_i = 30$	$\Sigma (X_i - \bar{X}) = 0$	$\Sigma (X_i - \bar{X})^2 = 40$

Thus:

$$s = \sqrt{\frac{1}{n} \Sigma (X_i - \bar{X})^2} = \sqrt{\frac{40}{5}} = \sqrt{8}$$
$$= 2.8$$

SAQ 23
Find the variance and standard deviation of children's ability scores for the first ten cases in the data set. Follow the method used in Table 19.

5.19 As with the mean deviation the standard deviation does fulfil the basic criteria for a measure of dispersion in that, if there is no variation between values in a distribution, it will give a value of zero and it will increase as the variation increases.

5.20 The above formulation of the variance and standard deviation leads to quite tedious and unnecessary computational problems if the mean is not a whole number. Thus it is usually preferable to use an equivalent alternative formulation which is given by the following:

$$s^2 = \frac{1}{n} \Sigma X_i^2 - (\overline{X})^2$$

i.e. it is the mean of the sum of squared values less the square of the mean of the values. Correspondingly the standard deviation is the square root of this quantity:

$$s = \sqrt{\frac{1}{n} \Sigma X_i^2 - (\overline{X})^2}$$

These formulae for the variance and standard deviation are directly equivalent to those given in paragraphs 5.16 and 5.17. The equivalence can be shown easily using some straightforward algebraic manipulations of the formulae, but here we are just interested in using the formulae.

5.21 An example of this use is given in Table 20 below, using the same data as in Table 19. You will see that the actual computation is much easier and requires only the calculation of the mean, $\overline{X}$, and the sum of squared values, ΣX_i^2 The resulting standard deviation has exactly the same value as that in Table 19 above.

Table 20   Alternative method of calculating the standard deviation

X_i (i)	X_i^2 (ii)
2	4
4	16
6	36
8	64
10	100
$\Sigma X_i = 30$	$\Sigma X_i^2 = 220$

Thus,   and

$$\overline{X} = \frac{1}{n} \Sigma X_i = \frac{30}{5} \qquad\qquad \Sigma X_i^2 = 220$$

$$= 6$$

Thus, the standard deviation is given by:

$$s = \sqrt{\left(\frac{\Sigma X_i^2}{n} - (\overline{X})^2\right)} = \sqrt{\frac{220}{5} - 36}$$

$$= \sqrt{(44 - 36)} = \sqrt{8}$$

$$= 2.8$$

SAQ 24
Find the variance and standard deviation of children's ability scores for the first ten cases in the data set. Follow the method used in Table 20.

5.22   In data analysis, the standard deviation is used in conjunction with the mean, and the kinds of considerations discussed in comparing the mean and median as descriptive measures carry over to a comparison of the standard deviation and the quartile deviation.

5.23   As with the mean, the standard deviation, unlike the quartile deviation, is strongly influenced by *extreme values* which can have a disproportionate effect on its size. The difference between the two measures will be greater the more dispersed the distribution is. Consider an extreme situation where we have ninety-nine values of five and one of 1005. Here the median would be five and the quartile deviation zero, which does represent 99% of the distribution. However, the mean would be 15 and the standard deviation 100.

extreme values

5.24   Thus, as with the median and mean, for descriptive purposes we would tend to use the quartile deviation when distributions are skewed, and the standard deviation otherwise. But, as was discussed in terms of the median in paragraph 4.33 above, the quartile deviation is similarly difficult to handle mathematically, and does lead to severe sampling problems as compared with the standard deviation.

Comparison of Measures of Variation

5.25   Most data analysis involves comparisons of groups, and measures of variation are needed to compare the relative *homogeneity* of different groups. But the absolute value for a measure of variation can be difficult to interpret. A standard deviation of twenty pounds in a distribution of annual incomes measured in thousands of pounds, would probably be considered small, while a corresponding figure for a distribution of weekly incomes which are measured in tens of pounds would be considered very large. A standard deviation of five points in an aptitude test marked out of 100 points would be interpreted quite differently from a similar standard deviation for a test marked out of twenty points. An additional problem arises when an attempt is made to compare the homogeneity of variation in measures using different units – thus the quartile deviations of incomes in Germany in terms of Deutschmarks is simply not comparable to that in the UK in terms of pounds. In order to compare measures of variation, they have to be placed in the relevant context.

homogeneity

5.26   One way to overcome this problem is to relate the measure of variation to an appropriate measure of location. There are two such measures. The first is the *coefficient of variation (cV)*, which relates the standard deviation to the mean as shown below:

coefficient of variation (cV)

$$cV = \frac{s}{\bar{X}}$$

or, alternatively, it can be presented as a percentage:

$$cV = \frac{s}{\bar{X}} \times 100$$

The idea is to express the value of the standard deviation of a distribution, not in absolute terms, but in proportionate terms relative to its own mean. The larger the resulting coefficient of variation then the greater the *heterogeneity* in the data and the smaller it is, then the greater the homogeneity.

heterogeneity

5.27 Thus, if the standard deviation of the distribution of annual incomes for one group of workers is $s = £300$ and the mean income $\bar{X} = £3000$, the coefficient of variation would be:

$$cV = \frac{s}{\bar{X}} = \frac{300}{3000}$$

$$= 0.1 \text{ or, alternatively, } 10\%$$

If the incomes for this first group are to be compared with those for a second group of workers where it is found that the standard deviation of incomes is also £300, it would be imprudent, to say the least, simply to conclude that the variation or degree of homogeneity in incomes is identical. For, if the mean income for the second group is £6000, then the coefficient of variation would be:

$$cV = \frac{300}{6000} = 0.05 \text{ (or 5\%)}$$

and a tentative conclusion may be drawn that the second group is more homogeneous in terms of income. On the other hand if the mean income of the second group is £1500, the coefficient of variation would be:

$$cV = \frac{300}{1500} = 0.20 \text{ (or 20\%)}$$

and the conclusions would obviously be quite different.

SAQ 25

Find the coefficient of variation for family income in SAQs 16 and 18 for the first ten cases in the data set. Note that you have already found the arithmetic mean. You now need to calculate the standard deviation.

5.28 An example of the use of this coefficient is found in Appendix 14, Table 1 of the Plowden Report, where the whole object is to assess the variations between Local Education Authorities in provision of education, measured over a wide range of indices. The author wishes to compare the variation in expenditure of teachers' salaries, non-teaching salaries, upkeep of grounds and building, debt charges, proportion of oversize classes, and other indices in both primary schools and secondary schools. Simply using the standard deviation for this purpose would be relatively meaningless, but using the coefficient of variation enables clear conclusions to be drawn. An extract from the Report is reproduced below as Table 21.

Table 21   Coefficients of variation of indices of provision of primary and secondary education among Local Authorities in England, 1961/2

Index	Coefficients of variation	
	Primary schools	Secondary schools
Expenditure on teachers' salaries[1]	7.2	7.2
Expenditure on non-teaching staff wages and salaries[1]	24.2	20.2
Expenditure on upkeep of grounds and buildings[1]	39.3	35.0
Expenditure on fuel, etc[1]	18.8	16.6
Expenditure on rent, rates, etc[1]	29.0	22.5
Expenditure on debt charges[1]	33.7	29.7
Total cost[1]	8.9	7.4
Proportion of oversize classes	53.3	16.3
Teachers released for special advanced training[2]	174.9	168.2

Source: Plowden Report, Appendix 14

Notes   [1] £ per pupil   [2] Per thousand teachers

SAQ 26
What conclusion do you draw from Table 21?

inter-quartile ratio (IQR),
quartile dispersion
coefficient

5.29 An alternative measure, used for the same reason as above but related to the quartile deviation as a measure of variation, is the *inter-quartile ratio* or *'quartile dispersion coefficient'*. It again relates the measure of dispersion to an appropriate measure of location and is given as:

$$IQR = \frac{\text{Inter-quartile range}}{\text{Median}}$$

$$= \frac{Q_3 - Q_1}{\tilde{X}}$$

For the following set of data,

$$2 \ 4 \ 6 \ 8 \ 10 \ 12 \ 14 \ 16$$

$\tilde{X} = 9$, $Q_1 = 5$ and $Q_3 = 13$. Thus,

$$IQR = \frac{Q_3 - Q_1}{\tilde{X}} = \frac{13 - 5}{9}$$

$$= \frac{8}{9} \simeq 0.89$$

As for the coefficient of variation, the larger the IQR of a given group, compared with that for other groups, then the greater would be the relative heterogeneity of the distribution.

SAQ 27
Find the inter-quartile ratio for family income for the first eight cases in the data set. See your answers to SAQs 14 and 21.

5.30 Table 22 gives a practical example of the use of the inter-quartile ratio. It shows the household income of households with different housing characteristics in Great Britain in 1971. There is some difference in the inter-quartile range of incomes for different housing groups, but the conclusions drawn from using the inter-quartile ratio are quite different.

Table 22 Household income (in £) for households in Great Britain, 1971

	Owned with mortgage	Owned outright	Local authority	Private rental unfurnished
Inter-quartile range	1 376	1 722	1 411	1 395
Median	2 430	1 480	1 611	1 325
Inter-quartile ratio	0.57	1.16	0.88	1.05

Source: Family Expenditure Survey, 1971

SAQ 28
What conclusions do you draw from Table 22?

6 Standardizing Individual Scores or Values

6.1 We have a number of times by now come across the problem of deciding whether a given statistic is 'high' or 'low' and of comparing statistics from different distributions and we have seen that, one way or another, we have to put the statistic into a relevant context. The same problem arises with individual scores or values. Is an income of £3000, or a mark of 6%, or an age of 30 years, high or low? In order to come to a decision we have to put the individual values of a variable into the context of the distribution from which they are derived. Thus, for example, an age of 30 years is high for full-time undergraduates but not for Open University students. We look at two approaches – the use of *standard scores* and of *percentiles*.

individual score

6.2 Take, for example, a boy who obtains 60 marks in a mathematics examination, and 50 marks in an English examination. Is he more able in mathematics than English? At first sight he is: his mark is higher in mathematics; but since these are different subjects it may be that one teacher is an 'easier' marker than the other. Thus we need to look at how the group as a whole perform in these examinations. To do this we can take each mark (X_i) away from the mean mark $\overline{X}$ from the group or subject. Now, if the mean in mathematics was 40 marks and in English 60 marks, then within this group he is above average in mathematics and below average in English – which more or less answers our original question.

6.3 But, what if the mean mark in mathematics is 55 and in English 45? He is now equally above average in each subject but we cannot necessarily regard these differences of 5 marks above average as being equivalent because the variations in the marks, i.e. the standard deviations, may differ between the groups. Thus some teachers may give marks over a limited range, others over a much wider range and the latter is often the case in mathematics.

6.4 Assume then that the standard deviation of the mathematics marks for all examineees is 10 marks and that of the English marks is 5 marks; then there would be a wider spread of marks in mathematics than in English and the overall distribution of marks in the two subjects might well be as shown in Figure 14 below. The effect of the different spreads of marks is that in mathematics a mark of 60 is quite close to the mean of 55 while a mark of 50 in English is comparatively much further away from the mean of 45.

Figure 14   Distribution of marks in mathematics and English examinations

(a)   Mathematics   (b)   English

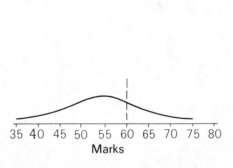
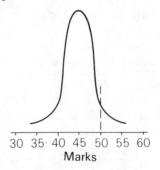

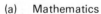

35 40 45 50 55 60 65 70 75 80
Marks

30 35 40 45 50 55 60
Marks

6.5 Thus, comparing 'raw' scores can be misleading: they have to be put into context and the characteristic of the distribution from which they came must be taken into account. This is done by calculating new 'scores' from the 'raw' data.

Such scores are known as *'standard'* or *'z-scores'* and are defined as:

where,

$$z_i = \frac{X_i - \bar{X}}{s}$$

and,

$$\bar{X} = \frac{1}{n} \Sigma X_i$$

$$s = \sqrt{\frac{1}{n} \Sigma X_i^2 - (\bar{X})^2} \qquad \text{(as defined above).}$$

6.6   Thus these 'standard' scores take into account both the mean and standard deviation of the distribution. In the example discussed above the mathematics score for the boy was $X_m = 60$; the mean mathematics mark was $\bar{X}_m = 55$ and the standard deviation $s_m = 10$. So that,

$$z_{maths} = \frac{X_m - \bar{X}_m}{s_m} = \frac{60 - 55}{10}$$
$$= 0.5$$

The mark attained in English was $X_e = 50$; the mean English mark was $\bar{X}_e = 45$ and the standard deviation $s_e = 5$. So that,

$$z_{english} = \frac{X_e - \bar{X}_e}{s_e} = \frac{50 - 45}{5}$$
$$= 1.0$$

6.7   Thus taking into account the distribution of marks, i.e. how the remainder of the pupils performed, the boy attained a higher standard score or performed better in English than in mathematics, since his score in English was 1 standard deviation above the mean English mark, whereas his score in mathematics was only $\frac{1}{2}$ standard deviation above the mean mathematics mark. The use of z-scores is a widely used standardizing procedure. The mean of the z-scores is always zero: $\bar{z} = 0$ and the standard deviation is $s_z = 1$. In a later Block you will see that they are particularly useful in conjunction with the *normal distribution* in the context of statistical inference.

SAQ 29
Find the arithmetic mean and standard deviation for the number of children per household for the first four cases in the data set. Calculate the respective z-scores for each case and show that the arithmetic mean of the z-scores, $\bar{z} = 0$; and the standard deviation of the z-scores, $s_z = 1$.

6.8   An alternative approach involves the notion of *percentiles* which have been mentioned earlier (paragraph 5.6). These are positional measures of a distribution, as are the median and quartiles, which divide a distribution of ordered values into 100 groups. In these terms, the median corresponds to the 50th percentile and the lower and upper quartiles correspond to the 25th and 75th percentiles respectively. Percentiles serve the same purpose as standard scores in facilitating the comparison of individual scores on two different tests or examinations, or on the same test or examination at different points in time; or of any variable of interest, e.g. incomes or ages at different times or places. We have discussed the method of finding percentiles earlier: given a frequency distribution, we have to construct a relative cumulative frequency distribution which shows the percentage of the frequency falling below (or above) a given value or score. In doing so, we can reduce the score on two different distributions to the same base and the same units – percentiles. Thus in Table 11 an income of £15 would be at the 30th percentile, an income of £30 would be at the 95th percentile and so on.

SAQ 30

By reference to the cumulative relative frequency distribution of the number of children per household which you calculated in the answer to SAQ 7, estimate the 20th, 60th, 90th and 95th percentiles.

6.9 An example of the use of percentiles occurs in Appendix 7 of the Plowden Report and an extract from one of the tables is shown below in Table 23. It shows the changes in scores in a reading comprehension test between 1948 and 1964, giving the scores at different percentiles.

Table 23   Percentile scores for pupils aged 11 on a reading comprehension test

| | Scores of pupils | |
Percentiles	1948	1964
90th	18.4	22.8
80th	15.9	20.5
70th	14.2	18.4
60th	12.7	16.4
50th	11.3	14.7
40th	9.8	13.0
30th	8.1	11.3
20th	6.6	9.4
10th	3.9	7.5

Source: Plowden Report, Appendix 7

SAQ 31

What conclusions do you draw from Table 23?

6.10 As mentioned earlier, positional measures such as percentiles are invariably used in describing and analysing income distributions. Such analyses often not only show the percentages of a population earning more than a given income but also the percentiles of total income earned by those above a given level of income. An example is given in Table 24 below, showing the distribution of

Table 24   Distribution of personal income (before tax) in the UK, 1973/4

Percentile of earners	Percentile of total earnings	Income range (lower limit)
		£
99th	93.5	7 195
95th	82.9	3 963
90th	73.2	3 260
80th	57.6	2 628
70th	44.7	2 208
60th	33.5	1 879
50th	24.2	1 550
40th	16.7	1 220
30th	10.9	944
20th	6.2	746
10th	2.7	549

Source: Royal Commission on the Distribution of Income and Wealth (1976) Second Report, Cmnd. 6626, HMSO

personal income in the United Kingdom in 1973/4. As can be seen, for example, the lowest 99% of earners earned 93.5% of total earnings, so that the top 1% of earners earned 6.5% of the total earnings in the UK and had a minimum income of £7195.

SAQ 32
What conclusions do you draw from Table 24?

6.11 As a final point you should note that such relative cumulative distributions can be presented diagrammatically by an ogive. In the case of Table 24, the percentile for earners can be compared with the percentile for total earnings, as shown in Figure 15.

Figure 15   Distribution of personal income (before tax) in the UK, 1973/4

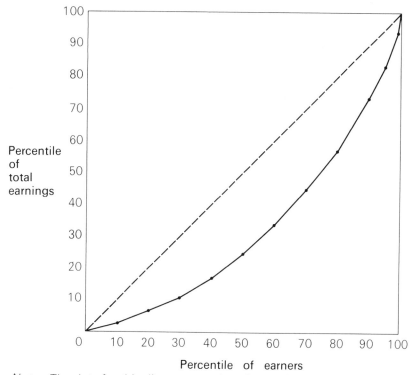

Percentile of total earnings

Percentile of earners

Note   The data for this diagram are given by the first two columns in Table 24

Source: Royal Commission on the Distribution of Income and Wealth (1976) Second Report, Comnd. 6626, HMSO

7   Ratios and Rates

7.1   You have now come across a number of different methods for comparing data relating to different individuals or groups. *Ratios* and *rates* are two simple measures which can be very useful for making comparisons. Suppose you are interested in comparing, say, the number of teachers employed by an authority at different types of schools, or the numbers of deaths in two or more towns. It is usually of more interest to compare the numbers of teachers in relation to the numbers of pupils in different types of schools, i.e. the pupil-teacher ratios, and to compare the numbers of deaths in two or more areas with the populations exposed to risk, i.e. the death rates.

7.2   The *ratio* of the number in one category A, to the number in a second **ratio**
category, B, is simply the number in category A divided by the number in
category B. Thus, for example, the *sex ratio* is usually given as the number of men **sex ratio**
in the group divided by the number of women. If there are equal numbers of men
and women, the sex ratio will be 1; if there are more men than women, it will be
greater than 1 and, if there are fewer men than women, it will be less than 1.
Appendix 1 of the Plowden Report describes a survey of teachers in primary and
secondary schools in England and Wales in 1964, 1042 men answered the survey
and 1197 women, so that the sex ratio in the sample was:

$$\frac{1042}{1197} = 0.87$$

Sometimes the ratio is multiplied by 100, which would give a result of 87. Another
way of putting it is to say that there were 0.87 men to every woman teacher, or 87
men to every 100 women teachers in the Plowden sample.

7.3   To illustrate the use of a ratio to summarize data and to bring out essential
points clearly, we can use some further data from Plowden which shows the sex of
the head and assistant teachers in different schools. Table 25 below shows the sex
ratio (men/women) for two grades of teacher in two types of school.

Table 25   Sex ratio of teachers, by grade of teacher and type of school

Type of school	Grade		Total
	Head	Assistant	
Infant	0.03	0.01	0.02
Infant/Junior	1.66	0.45	0.74
Junior	7.35	1.36	1.78
Secondary Modern	4.23	1.85	2.42

Source: Plowden Report, Appendix 1

Note   These data are based on the respondents in a survey of teachers

SAQ 33
What conclusions do you draw from Table 25?

7.4   Arithmetically speaking, a 'ratio' is simply a generic term implying
comparison by division of one number by another. Thus a proportion is a form of
ratio 'comparing' the number in a category with the total number in all relevant
categories, and an arithmetic mean is the ratio of total value and total
number. However, to avoid definitional complexities the term is usually reserved
for comparing one category with another quite different category.

7.5   A *rate* is also a way of comparing two categories by division – we have birth **rate**
rates, death rates, infant mortality rates, marriage rates, cancer rates, accident
rates, unemployment rates and so on. The idea of a rate is to compare the number
of occurrences of an event, such as birth or death, with the number of such events
which could possibly occur. So that:

$$\text{Rate} = \frac{\text{Number of events occurring in a given time period}}{\text{Number of such events which could have occurred}}$$

The resulting figure is often multiplied by a 100 or 1000. Thus, a rate attempts to
put a given statistic into a relevant context or to compare the number of events

occurring with the relevant population 'at risk'. Comparing the number of deaths in London and Bolton, for example, is rather pointless for most purposes, simply because London has a much larger population at 'risk'. Similarly in Baldamus' (1969) study of accidents, he is not interested in the crude numbers of accidents, but in the accident rate, the number of accidents per 1000 workers. Thus, for example, the crude death rate (*CDR*) for an administrative area, such as a country, town or region, is defined as:

$$CDR = \frac{\text{Number of deaths in a year}}{\text{Mid-year population}}$$

For England and Wales in 1971, the crude death rate was:

$$CDR = \frac{567\,262}{48\,902\,186} \times 1000$$
$$= 11.6$$

i.e. there were 11.6 deaths per 1000 persons.

7.6   There can often be a problem in finding the appropriate denominator for a rate. The crude birth rate, for example, is defined in a similar way to the death rate as: $\frac{\text{number of births}}{\text{mid-year population}}$. Thus, in 1920–30 in England and Wales the crude birth rate was 18.3, and it was very similar in 1962 at 17.9. But the birth rate as defined above does not take into account the difference in sex structure and age structure of the population at the two periods. A better measure of a changing birth rate would be to use the number of women aged 15–45 years as a denominator – as an indirect measure of the 'possible number of births'. If this is done the change in birth rate is quite different, being 73.9 in 1920–30 and 90.8 in 1962. Whereas the crude birth rate fell slightly, the revised birth rate has increased greatly. In this particular instance, it is partly because the number of women aged 15–45 as a percentage of the total population decreased quite sharply between the two periods.

8   Relationships

8.1   The presentation of descriptive statistical methods has so far been concerned with problems involving a single variable, and the comparison of the distribution of that variable between different groups. But frequently the most useful and interesting research and analytic questions involve more than one variable in a sample or population, and we are interested in the *relationship* between two (or more) variables. There are two kinds of questions one can ask about a relationship. Firstly, we can look at the nature of the structure of the relationship and try to build a *mathematical model* which represents it. In these situations, we specify one variable as the *'dependent' variable*, and one (or more) as the *independent or 'explanatory' variable*(s) and we attempt to explain variations in the dependent variable in terms of the selected 'explanatory' variable using what are called *'regression' models* or *'regression' analyses*. Alternatively, we can look at the relationship in terms of the interdependence, rather than the dependence, of two (or more) variables, and seek to measure the strength of a relationship by means of 'correlational' analysis. As will be seen in Blocks 6 and 7 these two types of questions and analyses are very closely related. But this section will look only at descriptive measures of *correlation* – the different ways in which the strength of a relationship can be described. In this section we shall consider only the simplest situations in which we attempt to describe the relationship between just two variables, although the underlying ideas can easily be extended to a consideration of relationships between three or more variables.

relationship

mathematical model, dependent variable, independent or explanatory variable, regression model, regression analysis

correlation

Correlation and Patterns of Association

8.2   In order to assess a possible relationship between two variables we need, as basic data, measurements on both variables for each of a number of individuals or units. As an example, take Table 26 below which shows for 10 pupils their IQ and mark gained in an examination. The simplest and usually the first step in attempting to see whether there is any relationship between IQ and test mark is to construct a scatter diagram, as in Figure 16. A scatter diagram takes one variable as the Y or vertical axis and the other as the X or horizontal axis, as shown. The

Table 26   IQ and examination scores of 10 pupils

IQ (X_i)	Mark (Y_i)
130	80
128	72
122	62
118	60
116	52
114	60
110	56
106	50
104	52
100	48

points then represent pairs of scores for each pupil, such as (114, 60). Unlike other graphs, we do *not* join these points up. The interest lies in the pattern or scatter which the points take. If you have any difficulty in understanding the construction of scatter diagrams, you will find a full explanation in the Developmental and Diagnostic Booklet (DDB).

Figure 16

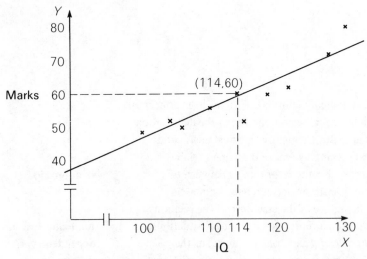

8.3   As might be expected, there is no perfect *one-to-one relationship* between IQ and marks, and a higher IQ does not necessarily mean a higher mark. For example, a score of 52 was achieved by a pupil with an IQ of 104, and also by a pupil with an IQ of 116. But on the other hand, there does seem to be a general relationship in that, taking the data as a whole, the lower IQ scores do tend to be associated with the lower marks, and the higher IQ scores with the higher marks. Moreover, if we draw freehand, as in the diagram, a straight line through the 'middle' of the points, we do find that the points cluster around this line fairly closely. This latter point is very important, for this concept of *linearity*, the

one-to-one relationship

linearity

tendency for a set of data on a scatter diagram to approximate a straight line, lies at the centre of the concept of a *correlation coefficient*.

correlation coefficient

8.4 Of course, Figure 16 shows only one possible pattern of relationship between two variables. There are many others and some are given in Figure 17 (a) – (e) below. In (a) all the points lie on a straight line: there is a one-to-one relationship between Y values and X values so that the Y scores are entirely predictable from the X scores, and *vice versa*. Moreover, low scores on X are associated with low scores on Y and high scores on X with high scores on Y and this is called *perfect positive correlation*. In Figure 17 (b) the situation is similar except that the slope of the line is reversed and low scores on X are associated with high scores on Y and high scores on X with low scores on Y; all the points fall on the straight line and this kind of relationship is known as *perfect negative correlation*.

perfect positive correlation

perfect negative correlation

8.5 These 'perfect' situations rarely, if ever, occur in practice, and situations such as those in Figure 17(c) and (d) are much more likely. In both cases, the points do not all fall on a straight line but are spread around it, often in the form of an ellipse, as shown. In (c) the points tend to cluster closely around the straight line which rises from left to right; this indicates a relatively *high positive correlation*. In (d) the points are much more scattered about a downward trending line which falls from left to right; this indicates a *low negative correlation*. In (e) the situation is quite different, for there is no apparent relationship between X and Y values; low values of X are equally likely to occur with low and high values of Y. There is no discernible linear relationship and a knowledge of X tells us nothing about Y; there is *zero correlation*.

high positive correlation

low negative correlation

zero correlation

Figure 17

(a)   Perfect positive correlation

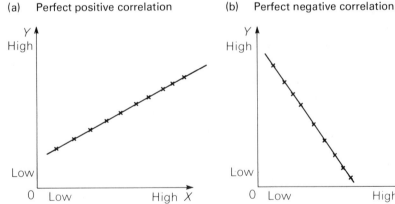

(b)   Perfect negative correlation

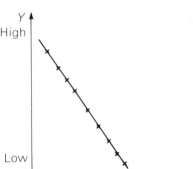

(c)   High positive correlation

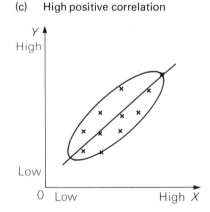

(d)   Low negative correlation

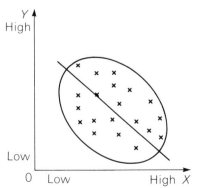

(e)   Zero correlation

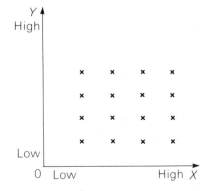

SAQ 34

For the first ten cases in the data set, draw scatter diagrams for the pairs of variables:

(a) Child's ability score (Y) and family income (X)

(b) Child's ability score (Y) and number of children in household (X)

(c) Family income (Y) and number of children in household (X).

Comment on the relationships you have found.

Pearson's Product Moment Correlation Coefficient

8.6 The above discussion has illustrated some of the different configurations of data in scatter diagrams and the different strengths of relationship possible. The relationship between X and Y was perfect in Figures 17(a) and (b), less than perfect in (c), weak in (d) and non-existent in (e). What is needed is a means of measuring the strength of a relationship, a coefficient of correlation. By far the most important coefficient and the one which will be considered here is *Pearson's product moment correlation coefficient*. It has many desirable properties. Its value can only lie between $+1$ and -1, where $+1$ signifies a perfect positive linear relationship as in (a) above, and -1 signifies perfect negative linear relationship as in (b) above. It will be zero in any situation where there is no linear association as in (e) above. It will have a high positive value (close to 1) for (c) and a negative value close to 0 for (d). But before we find out how it is calculated, let us first see how it is derived and, in so doing, discover *why* it has the above characteristics.

Pearson's product moment correlation coefficient

8.7 As a starting point, we might think of correlation as the degree to which variation in one variable corresponds to or is related to variation in another, and this leads to the idea of *covariation*. Now one way of 'measuring' covariation is to look at the variation in the value of each variable in terms of the differences of each value from its appropriate arithmetic mean. For each pair of values we can take $(X_i - \overline{X})$ and $(Y_i - \overline{Y})$ and compare each pair of differences. This is essentially what is accomplished by a statistical measure known as the *covariance* – it multiplies the two differences for each point or observation, and sums the resulting 'cross-products'. The sum is then divided by the number of observations; this is necessary since the resulting statistic would otherwise depend on the number of observations rather than the degree of relationship expressed by the sum of the cross-products. The covariance, *Cov*, can then be written as:

covariation

covariance (*Cov*)

$$Cov = \frac{1}{n} \Sigma (X_i - \overline{X}) (Y_i - \overline{Y})$$

where n is the number of observations, $\overline{X}$ is the mean of the X variable and $\overline{Y}$ is the mean of the Y variable. How does this help? As we shall see, the covariance does fulfil some of the desirable criteria for a correlation coefficient. It will have a value of zero when there is no linear relationship; it will take positive and negative values in situations where the data show evidence of corresponding to a positive or negative linear trend and covariance will increase or decrease as the strength of the relationship, or tendency to perfect linearity, increases or decreases.

8.8 Figure 18 shows a scatter diagram divided into four quadrants by axes drawn through the mean of the X variable and the mean of the Y variable. Taking quadrant I first, for any point falling in this quadrant such as (X_1, Y_1) any value Y such as Y_1, will be larger than its mean $\overline{Y}$ so that $(Y_1 - \overline{Y})$ is positive, any X value such as X_1 will be larger than its mean $\overline{X}$, and $(X_1 - \overline{X})$ is positive. Thus, the product $(X_1 - \overline{X})(Y_1 - \overline{Y})$ is a product of two positive quantities and so will be

50

positive. The contribution to covariance of any pair of values in quadrant I such as (X_1, Y_1) will thus be positive. Similarly, the contribution to covariance of any point which falls in quadrant III will be positive because $(X_i - \bar{X})$ will be negative and also $(Y_i - \bar{Y})$ will be negative; the resulting product of two negative quantities will be positive (see DDB). For any point which falls in quadrant II $(Y_i - \bar{Y})$ will be positive, $(X_i - \bar{X})$ will be negative; the product of two such quantities will be negative and so will their contribution to covariance. For points falling in quadrant IV $(Y_i - \bar{Y})$ will be negative and $(X_i - \bar{X})$ will be positive, so their product will be negative and their contribution to covariance will be negative. Figure 18 summarizes these relationships between the part of the scatter diagram in which a data point falls and whether, as a consequence, its contribution to covariance is positive or negative.

Figure 18

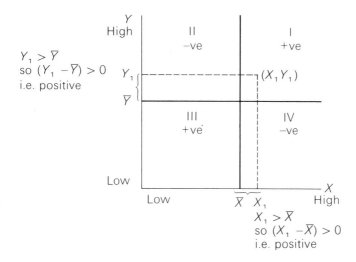

8.9 Thus, the cross-products contributing to covariance will vary depending upon where in the scatter diagram each point falls. As a result, different scatters will have different values of covariance. Figure 19 shows scatter diagrams with three different ellipses superimposed, each representing a scatter of points. In Figure 19(a) there is a positive relationship and, as can be seen, the positive values contributing to covariance will outweigh the negative values, giving a positive covariance. In (b) the reverse is true and the covariance will be negative. In (c), however, there is no linear association and the positive and negative values will tend to cancel each other out giving a covariance of zero, or at least a very low value. In addition it could also be shown that, for both positive and negative relationships, the closer the observations approximate to a straight line, the larger would be the value of the covariance.

Figure 19

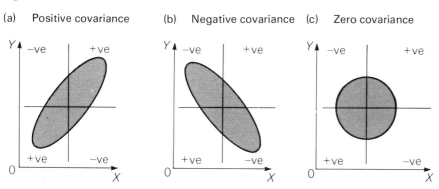

51

8.10   A method of calculating the covariance is shown in Table 27, for five pairs of observations on two variables, X and Y. The first step is to find the mean of the X_i which are given in column (i); then in column (ii) each X_i has its mean, $\bar{X}$, subtracted from it. A similar procedure is carried out for the Y variable in columns (iii) and (iv) respectively. Finally in column (v) the two sets of differences are multiplied and the results summed. The scatter diagram for the data of Table 27 is shown in Figure 20.

Table 27   A method of calculating the covariance

X_i (i)	$(X_i - \bar{X})$ (ii)	Y_i (iii)	$(Y_i - \bar{Y})$ (iv)	$(X_i - \bar{X})(Y_i - \bar{Y})$ (v) = (ii) × (iv)
1	− 2	1	− 2	+ 4
2	− 1	3	0	0
3	0	2	− 1	0
4	+ 1	5	+ 2	+ 2
5	+ 2	4	+ 1	+ 2
15	0	15	0	+ 8

To begin with we calculate:

$$\bar{X} = \frac{1}{n}\Sigma X_i = \frac{15}{5} \qquad \bar{Y} = \frac{1}{n}\Sigma Y_i = \frac{15}{5}$$
$$= 3 \qquad\qquad\qquad = 3$$

After calculating column (v) we can then find the covariance:

$$Cov = \frac{1}{n}\Sigma (X_i - \bar{X})(Y_i - \bar{Y}) = \frac{1}{5} \cdot 8$$
$$= + 1.6$$

Figure 20

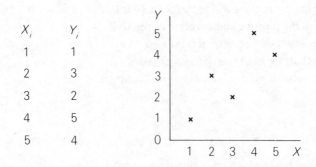

X_i	Y_i
1	1
2	3
3	2
4	5
5	4

SAQ 35
Calculate the covariance (Cov) between the variables family income (X) and child's ability score (Y) for the first ten cases in the data set. Note that the arithmetic means have been calculated in the answer to SAQ 16.

8.11   You will encounter the covariance again in Block 7, but as a measure of relationship it is, in itself, only of limited value, and can be difficult to interpret. To begin with, its value depends on the type of units being used. Consider a set of data showing the incomes and ages of a number of individuals; with annual income and age in years we can calculate the covariance as a measure of relationship. If we changed the data to weekly income and age in years, the covariance would be much smaller; the value of the covariance changes, not because the underlying relationship between income and age has changed but simply because the numerical value of annual income is larger than the value of weekly income. In addition, the covariance has no set upper or lower values which we can use to judge the strength of a relationship. Thus in Table 27, we cannot say whether a result of $Cov = + 1.6$ denotes a strong or weak relationship between X and Y.

8.12   A statistic is needed which will overcome these problems and it is given by a simple adaptation of the covariance. It is a standardization procedure which is analogous to the methods discussed in a seemingly different context in section 7. All that is done is to divide the covariance (Cov) by the standard deviation, s_x, and the standard deviation, s_y, as shown in the formula below. It is beyond the scope of this section to give a proof, but the effect is that the resulting statistic has all the desirable characteristics of the covariance, plus the added advantages that it is unaffected by the units used and will never exceed a maximum value of $+ 1$ or a minimum value of $- 1$. A value of $+ 1$ will be attained in the case of a perfect positive linear relationship and $- 1$ in the case of a perfect negative linear relationship. This statistic is Pearson's product moment correlation coefficient and is represented by r. Thus:

$$r = \frac{Cov}{s_x s_y}$$

where

$$s_x = \sqrt{\frac{1}{n} \Sigma X_i^2 - \bar{X}^2}$$

$$s_y = \sqrt{\frac{1}{n} \Sigma Y_i^2 - \bar{Y}^2}$$

and

$$Cov = \frac{1}{n} \Sigma (X_i - \bar{X})(Y_i - \bar{Y})$$

8.13   However, for computational purposes, it is more convenient to use an alternative form of the covariance which can be derived from the above. Either method will reach the same numerical answer. The preferred form of the covariance is:

$$Cov = \frac{1}{n} \Sigma XY - (\bar{X})(\bar{Y})$$

For computational purposes, the correlation coefficient is:

$$r = \frac{\frac{1}{n} \Sigma XY - (\bar{X})(\bar{Y})}{\sqrt{\left(\frac{1}{n} \Sigma X^2 - (\bar{X})^2\right)\left(\frac{1}{n} \Sigma Y^2 - (\bar{Y})^2\right)}}$$

8.14   An example of a calculation of the correlation coefficient is shown below in Table 28 for the data of Table 27 and Figure 20. Notice that $\bar{X}, \bar{Y}, \Sigma X^2, \Sigma Y^2$ and ΣXY need to be calculated in order to find the covariance, and the two variances. The value of the covariance given in Table 28 is the same as that found using a different method of calculation, in Table 27. The correlation is positive, as might

be judged from the scatter diagram, and is reasonably strong, because the value of
+ 0.8 is quite close to + 1.0.

Table 28   Calculation of a correlation coefficient for data in Figure 20

X_i (i)	Y_i (ii)	X_i^2 (iii)	Y_i^2 (iv)	X_iY_i (v)
1	1	1	1	1
2	3	4	9	6
3	2	9	4	6
4	5	16	25	20
5	4	25	16	20
$\Sigma X_i = 15$	$\Sigma Y_i = 15$	$\Sigma X_i^2 = 55$	$\Sigma Y_i^2 = 55$	$\Sigma X_iY_i = 53$

To begin with we calculate:

$$\overline{X} = \frac{1}{n}\Sigma X_i = \frac{1}{5}\cdot 15 \qquad\qquad \overline{Y} = \frac{1}{n}\Sigma Y_i = \frac{1}{5}\cdot 15$$
$$= 3 \qquad\qquad\qquad\qquad = 3$$

Next, since $r = \dfrac{Cov}{s_x s_y}$, we need to find Cov, s_x and s_y.

$$Cov = \frac{1}{n}\Sigma XY - (\overline{X})(\overline{Y}) = \frac{53}{5} - (3)(3) = +1.6$$

$$s_x = \sqrt{\frac{1}{n}\Sigma X^2 - (\overline{X})^2} = \sqrt{\frac{55}{5} - (3)^2} = \sqrt{2} = 1.414$$

$$s_y = \sqrt{\frac{1}{n}\Sigma Y^2 - (\overline{Y})^2} = \sqrt{\frac{55}{5} - (3)^2} = \sqrt{2} = 1.414$$

Thus Pearson's product moment correlation coefficient is:

$$r = \frac{Cov}{s_x s_y} = \frac{+1.6}{(1.414)(1.414)} = +\frac{1.6}{2} = +0.8$$

SAQ 36
Calculate the product moment correlation coefficient for the variables family
income (X) and child's ability score (Y). Some of the relevant calculations can be
found in the answers to SAQs 23, 25 and 35.

8.15   Correlation analysis is an essential tool in all the social sciences, and
extensive use is made of it in the Plowden Report. Take, for example,
Appendix 14. As mentioned earlier, the objective was to analyse variations in
standards of 'provision' of educational resources in Local Education Authorities,
and variations in output. 'Provision' is expressed in terms of a number of indices
such as costs of teachers' salaries per pupil and percentage of oversize classes,
and output by such indices as the percentage of pupils staying on at school, and
the number of Teacher Training entrants per head of population. The whole point

of the analysis is to look at the interrelationship between 'provision' and 'output' and in addition to see how, if at all, these various indices are related to a large set of indices of social conditions such as occupational structure and housing conditions. Thus, correlation methods are the essential tools in the analysis. Table 29 below gives an extract from one of the tables in Appendix 14.

Table 29   Correlation of indices of standard of provision of primary school education and output indices for Local Education Authorities in England 1961/2

Standards of provision	Output indices		
	Pupils aged 17 as % of those aged 13, four years before (i)	Total new awards to university/ population 17–19 (ii)	Teacher Training entrants/ population 17–19 (iii)
(i) Cost of teachers' salaries/pupil	+ 0.32	+ 0.22	+ 0.16
(ii) Total costs/pupil	+ 0.16	+ 0.00	+ 0.00
(iii) Percentage oversize classes	− 0.18	− 0.17	− 0.16

Source: Plowden Report, Appendix 14

SAQ 37
What conclusions do you draw from Table 29?

Interpreting the Correlation Coefficient

8.16   There are a number of points which have to be borne in mind in interpreting the correlation coefficient. To begin with, as has been emphasized, the correlation coefficient is a measure of strength of a *linear* relationship: its value depends on the degree to which the data approximate a straight line. The problem is that in some situations there may be a strong relationship but that the relationship is not linear – it cannot be sensibly approximated by a straight line. In an extreme case, the data might conform to a U-shaped distribution as in Figure 21(a) below. Here the covariance and, therefore, the product moment correlation coefficient would be very small or zero, while in fact the relationship is strong, but non-linear. On the other hand, Figure 21(b) shows a relationship which may well give a reasonably sized linear correlation, but which could be misinterpreted since there is a strong relationship although it too is not linear. The lesson to be learned is that the product moment correlation coefficient should only be calculated *after* a scatter diagram has been drawn, and after a decision has been reached that a straight line can reasonably be said to approximate the relationship.

Figure 21

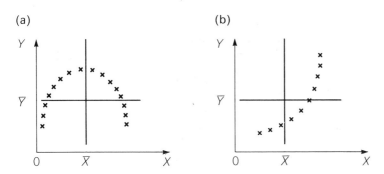

55

8.17 There are many ways of overcoming this problem of non-linear correlation – there are measures of non-linear correlation such as the correlation ratio, or the data can be 'transformed' to approximate a straight line. But these are outside the scope of this Block, and you should remember that while statistical independence as portrayed in Figure 17(e) will lead to a zero correlation, a zero correlation does not imply statistical independence, i.e. that there is no relationship, but only that there is no *linear* relationship between the variables. There may or may not be a non-linear relationship.

8.18 Secondly, coefficients of $+1$ or -1 have quite strict and definite interpretations. Also, any non-zero coefficient indicates some degree of linear relationship and $r = 0.6$ shows a stronger linear relationship than $r = 0.3$. But any further interpretation can be difficult because we cannot say $r = 0.6$ shows 'twice' the degree of relationship shown by $r = 0.3$; neither can we say that the difference between $r = 0.1$ and $r = 0.2$ is 'the same as' or equal to the difference between $r = 0.8$ and $r = 0.9$. The correlation is not measured on a linear scale with equal units; it corresponds more to measures on an ordinal scale where the data can simply be ranked. We have to leave the problem at this point but it will be tackled again in Blocks 6 and 7. There you will find that, notwithstanding some difficulty in interpreting r, r^2 has a very definite and precise interpretation where $r^2 = 0.36$ can be considered as twice $r^2 = 0.18$; r^2 is extremely important in relation to regression analysis which is dealt with in Block 7.

8.19 Thirdly, in Block 1 you have come across the concept of *causation* in the social sciences. It is quite a common error to confuse correlation with causation. It is important to remember that a correlation coefficient is simply a number, a mathematical construct which shows a relationship between two sets of measures. It does not in itself imply any *causal relationship*. Given simply a correlation coefficient between variables A and B, it is equally likely or unlikely that A causes B, B causes A, or that a third factor C causes the relationship between A and B. On the other hand, causation does imply the existence of '*concomitant variations*', that A does vary with changes in B. But even here one has in practice to be very careful since the correlation coefficient can be zero, for non-linear relationships. The confusion between causation and correlation has given rise to many instances of 'nonsense' correlation or *spurious correlations* such as the strong correlation to be found between storks sighted and the number of births in North Germany; whisky production and the number of teachers; size of feet and the quality of handwriting. Hopefully no one is going to take a high correlation as evidence that an increase in storks 'causes' a rise in births. The correlation is high simply because both are related to the number of dwellings which is related to the size and development of towns and cities. Similarly, whisky production and teachers are both related to rising standards of living and size of feet and handwriting are both related to age of children.

causation

causal relationship

concomitant variation

spurious correlation

8.20 The fourth point is that a further problem can arise when the researcher is not clear about which units of analysis are appropriate and confuses correlations between groups on two variables with correlations between individuals who compose those groups. They are not the same, and the error of making inferences concerning the relationship between two variables among individuals from similar variables measured among groups is called the *ecological fallacy*. This fallacy was pointed out quite clearly by Robinson in 1950. Amongst regions of the United States he found that the correlation between the percentage of foreign-born and the percentage of illiteracy was -0.62. But this does not imply that the foreign-born tended to be less literate, for when the correlation for individuals was calculated it came to $+0.12$.

ecological fallacy

8.21 The last point is another reminder that it is always best to look at a scatter diagram of the data before calculating a coefficient, for it may tell you something about the structure of the data. Figure 22 is an example. Such a pattern may well give a relatively high correlation, but using it blindly we would miss the fact that it is high because we have two separate groups even though within each group the correlation seems to be low. Alternatively, Figure 23 shows a different pattern where the correlation may be small, in spite of the fact that the majority of the observations seem to be linearly related. The problem here is that (as we found with means and variances) the correlation coefficient is sensitive to extreme values or outliers.

8.22 Figure 24 illustrates another, possibly misleading, situation which can arise in correlation analysis. In analysing relationships between two variables we must always be careful to notice whether the data available cover the whole or only a part of the range of the variables concerned. Thus if our study had taken only values falling below A on the X axis then we might well have concluded that there was no association between Y and X, whilst if we had calculated the correlation between the variables over the whole range of X and Y, we would have found evidence of a positive linear relationship.

Figure 22

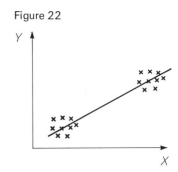

Figure 23

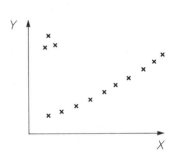

Figure 24

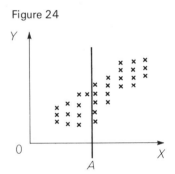

Other Measures of Correlation

8.23 Pearson's product moment correlation coefficient measures the strength and direction of a relationship for two variables both of which are measured on an interval or ratio scale. But, of course, many variables encountered in social research are measured on ordinal or nominal scales, and in analysing a data set it may be necessary to measure the relationship between two nominal variables or between two ordinal variables and sometimes between other combinations of variables. In such circumstances, Pearson's product moment correlation coefficient cannot be used, and alternative measures of correlation have been developed. We shall consider next one type of correlation coefficient for each of three different situations: *Spearman's Rank Correlation Coefficient* (r_s) as a measure of association between two ordinal variables; the *Point Biserial Coefficient* (r_{pb}) as a measure of association between one dichotomous nominal variable and one interval or ratio variable; the *Phi Coefficient* (∅) as a measure of association between two dichotomous variables.

Spearman's Rank Correlation Coefficient

8.24 When both variables yield ordinal measures, *Spearman's rank correlation coefficient* (r_s) can be used to assess the strength of the relationship. Raw data can be converted into rankings, or ranks may be gathered as original data. With such data, we look for patterns such as, if A has a higher rank than B on variable X, does A also have a higher rank on variable Y? The coefficient takes the value of zero when there is no relationship between the variables, + 1.0 if the rankings are in perfect positive correspondence or agreement as in (a) below, and − 1.0 if there is a perfect negative correspondence or disagreement as in (b) below.

Spearman's rank correlation coefficient (r_s)

```
                        Ranks
(a) Perfect agreement    X: 1 2 3 4 5
                         Y: 1 2 3 4 5
(b) Perfect disagreement X: 1 2 3 4 5
                         Y: 5 4 3 2 1
```

The formula for computing Spearman's rank correlation coefficient is:

$$r_s = 1 - \frac{6\,\Sigma\,D_i^2}{n\,(n^2 - 1)}$$

where n is the number of individuals or pairs of observations and $D_i = (X_i - Y_i)$ or the difference between the ranking of the ith individual on the two variables. The formula can be derived by taking the formula for the product moment correlation coefficient and applying it to ranks rather than scores.

8.25 Table 30 shows a teacher's ranking of 5 pupils in terms of their ability in mathematics (X) and English (Y). In mathematics, the teacher was unable to distinguish between the two least able pupils so they have been allocated to a *tied ranking*. When ranks are 'tied' in this way, each is given the 'average' of the ranks involved; in this case each is given a rank of $4\frac{1}{2}$. Similarly if the three least able pupils had 'tied' then each would have been given the rank of 4. In order to calculate r_s, the first step is to find the differences in the rankings for each pupil (column (iii)); these differences are then squared and summed (column (iv)), and finally the sum is substituted into the formula.

tied ranking

Table 30   Calculation of r_s

Mathematics X_i (i)	English Y_i (ii)	D_i $= (X_i - Y_i)$ (iii)	D_i^2 $= (X_i - Y_i)^2$ (iv)
1	4	-3	9
2	3	-1	1
3	5	-2	4
$4\frac{1}{2}$	1	$+3\frac{1}{2}$	12.25
$4\frac{1}{2}$	2	$+2\frac{1}{2}$	6.25

$$\Sigma\,D_i^2 = 32.5$$

The number of pupils, $n = 5$

and

$$\Sigma D_i^2 = 32.5$$

Thus,

$$r_s = 1 - \frac{6\,\Sigma\,D_i^2}{n(n^2 - 1)} = 1 - \frac{6 \times 32.5}{5\,(5^2 - 1)}$$

$$= 1 - \frac{195}{5 \times 24} = 1 - \frac{195}{120}$$

$$= 1 - 1.625$$

$$= -0.625$$

8.26 In this example, there is a modest negative relationship between the two variables. In the opinion of the teacher, and for these pupils, ability in mathematics and English are *inversely related*.

inverse relation

SAQ 38
Using the formula given in the text and applying it to the first six cases in the data set, find the rank correlation coefficient (r_s) between the variables 'occupation of father' and 'attitude of parents to part-time job'.

The Point Biserial Coefficient

8.27 The second case to be considered is one where there is one dichotomous, nominal variable and one interval or ratio variable. Thus the sex of children may be related to examination marks, or ability scores may be related to whether schools are streamed or unstreamed.

8.28 Suppose that the X variable is a dichotomy with n_0 observations in category 0 and n_1 observations in category 1, so that the total number of observations is:

$$n = n_0 + n_1$$

Suppose that Y is an interval variable with n observations and an overall mean of $\bar{Y}$ and a standard deviation of s_y. In addition, the mean of the Y variable for category 1 alone is $\bar{Y}_1$. Then the *point biserial correlation coefficient* between X and Y is defined by:

point biserial correlation coefficient (r_{pb})

$$r_{pb} = \sqrt{\frac{n_1}{n_0}} \times \frac{(\bar{Y}_1 - \bar{Y})}{s_y}$$

8.29 This coefficient can range between $+1.0$ and -1.0 and take a value of zero when there is no relationship; this occurs when $\bar{Y}_1 = \bar{Y}$, i.e. when both categories on the nominal variable have the same mean on the interval variable. If all those in category 1 were given a 'score' of 1 and those in category 0 a 'score' of zero, then the above formula could be derived from the product moment correlation coefficient between X and Y (Pearson's r).

8.30 An example can be taken from Appendix 3 of the Plowden Report to assess the relationship between the social class, X, of the fathers of pupils in primary schools with the age, Y, at which the father completed his formal education (TEA or Terminal Education Age). Social class is dichotomized into non-manual (category 1) and manual (category 0). Simplifying the data for computational purposes, there is a sample of $n = 1000$ fathers of whom $n_1 = 300$ are non-manual and $n_0 = 700$ are manual. The mean TEA for non-manual fathers is $\bar{Y}_1 = 16.1$ and the mean TEA for all the fathers in the sample is $\bar{Y} = 15.2$ with a variance of $s_y^2 = 2.2$. Thus, the correlation between social class and terminal education age is given by:

$$r_{pb} = \sqrt{\frac{n_1}{n_0}} \times \frac{(\bar{Y}_1 - \bar{Y})}{s_y}$$

$$n_1 = 300$$
$$n_0 = 700$$
$$\bar{Y}_1 = 16.1$$
$$\bar{Y} = 15.2$$
$$s_y = \sqrt{2.2}$$

$$r_{pb} = \sqrt{\frac{300}{700}} \times \frac{(16.1 - 15.2)}{\sqrt{2.2}}$$

$$\simeq +0.4$$

As might be expected there is a modest positive correlation between non-manual occupation and terminal education age.

SAQ 39
For the first ten cases in the data set, find the point biserial correlation coefficient between the 'sex of child' and 'child's ability score'.

The Phi Coefficient

8.31   Assume now that we have a set of data measured on a nominal scale, and that the variable only has two categories, i.e. is dichotomous. There are numerous such sets of data in the Plowden Report. As an example, consider the data in Table 32 which show the relationship between X, social class of parents in junior school defined as manual or non-manual, with whether the parents did or did not wish the child to go to a Grammar school, Y. (The numbers in the table have been simplified for calculation purposes.) This type of table is often called a *contingency table*. Ignoring sampling errors, the data in this table do seem to provide some evidence of an association between social class and school, for if we percentage the table we find that 70% of non-manual parents but only 50% of manual parents wanted their child to go to Grammar school.

contingency table

8.32   Given that we can see some association, the *Phi coefficient* (Ø) can be used to measure the strength of the relationship. It can be derived in two ways, but the first involves a knowledge of a statistic of association called χ^2 (Chi-squared), which is outside the scope of this Block. The second approach is to derive Ø from the product moment correlation coefficient. It involves the use of dummy variables by scoring each dichotomy as 1 or 0 as shown in Table 31. In theory it is of no consequence which category is labelled 0 and which is labelled 1. In Table 31 the n cases in the data set are allocated to the four cells of the contingency table as shown with the numbers represented by the letters, a, b, c and d. Clearly $n = a + b + c + d$. The marginal column at the right shows that for the Y variable, $(a + b)$ cases take the value 1 and $(c + d)$ take the value 0. For the X variable, $(a + c)$ cases take the value 1 and $(b + d)$ take the value 0.

Phi coefficient (ø)

Table 31

	X		
	1	0	
Y 1	a	b	$a + b$
0	c	d	$c + d$
	$a + c$	$b + d$	n

8.33   In terms of the dummy values the arithmetic mean of the Y variable is:

$$\overline{Y} = \frac{1(a + b) + 0(c + d)}{n} = \frac{a + b}{n}$$

which is just the proportion of cases falling in the 1 category of the Y variable. Similarly the mean of X in terms of dummy values is:

$$\overline{X} = \frac{a + c}{n}$$

8.34   By applying the usual formulae for the calculation of variances and covariances and substituting dummy values it is possible to arrive at the following expressions for the variances and covariance in terms of the quantities which appear in the margins of the contingency table:

$$s_y^2 = \frac{(a + b)(c + d)}{n}$$

$$s_x^2 = \frac{(a + c)(b + d)}{n}$$

$$Cov = \frac{a - (a + b)(a + c)}{n}$$

The algebra involved is rather tedious, but if these quantities are substituted into the usual formula for the calculation of the Pearson product moment correlation coefficient we arrive at the measure of association between the dichotomous variables X and Y which is the Phi coefficient, given by:

$$\emptyset = \frac{ad - bc}{\sqrt{(a+b)(c+d)(a+c)(b+d)}}$$

Table 32   Social class of father and type of secondary school desired for child

		Social class (X)		
		Non-manual	Manual	Total
School desired (Y)	Grammar	21	35	56
	Non-Grammar	9	35	44
	Total	30	70	100

8.35   For the data in Table 32, we have:

$$(a+b) = 56 \qquad (c+d) = 44$$
$$(a+c) = 30 \qquad (b+d) = 70$$

And, $a = 21$, $b = 35$, $c = 9$, $d = 35$. Then,

$$\emptyset = \frac{21 \times 35 - 35 \times 9}{\sqrt{56 \times 44 \times 30 \times 70}} = \frac{735 - 315}{\sqrt{5\ 174\ 400}} = \frac{420}{2275}$$

$$= +0.18$$

8.36   Notice that in this example we have taken the category non-manual with the value 1 and manual with the value zero, Grammar school with value 1 and non-Grammar with zero and as a result Phi has a small positive value indicating a positive association or correlation between these variables. This has no intrinsic meaning, and can only be interpreted in terms of how unity and zero were allocated. In this case a positive correlation shows that the two categories labelled 'unity' are related, as are the two categories labelled zero, i.e. Grammar and non-manual are related, as are non-Grammar and manual. A negative result would have implied unity-zero relationships.

8.37   Finally, you should note that $\emptyset$ has a strict definition of a perfect association. A value of $\emptyset = +1$ can only occur if both diagonal cells (1,0) and (0,1) are empty of observations; a value of -1 can only occur if both diagonal cells (1,1) and (0,0) are empty of observations. Table 33 (a) shows a situation in which $\emptyset = +1$; Table 33 (b) shows the situation when only one diagonal cell is empty and in such circumstances a value of $\emptyset = +1$ or -1 cannot be achieved so the association between the two variables must be less than perfect.

Table 33

(a)

		X		
		1	0	
Y	1	50	0	50
	0	0	50	50
		50	50	100

(b)

		X		
		1	0	
Y	1	50	20	70
	0	0	30	30
		50	50	100

SAQ 40

Take the first ten cases in the data set for the two variables 'occupation of father' (X) and 'child's ability score' (Y) and construct dichotomous variables from the categories and scores given as follows:

(a)   Construct a dichotomous social class variable by aggregating Social Classes I, II and III (Non-manual) to be called 'Non-manual', taking the value 1 and by aggregating Social Classes III (Manual), IV and V to be called 'Manual' and taking the value 0.

(b)   Construct a dichotomous 'ability' variable by allocating the value 1 to those children scoring above average (mean = 50) and to be called 'more able'; allocate the value 0 to those children scoring below average (50) and to be called 'less able'.

(c)   Set out the data in the form of a contingency table and calculate the value of $\emptyset$ to see whether there is any association between social class of father and the child's ability score.

Objectives

After studying this Part you should be able to:

1 Define a variable (paragraph 1.2, 1.15, 1.16).

2 Explain the distinction between nominal, ordinal, interval and ratio data (paragraphs 1.6–1.14).

3 Given a set of data, identify the level of measurement (paragraphs 1.13–1.16, SAQ 1).

4 Tabulate a frequency distribution and display it in the form of a histogram (section 2, paragraphs 3.5–3.8).

5 Describe the use of rates and ratios and other methods of standardization for comparing two sets of data (sections 6 and 7).

6 Define the mean, median and mode of a frequency distribution and calculate for ungrouped data (section 4).

7 Give examples of distributions where mean and median will be sharply separated and explain why (paragraphs 4.20–4.22, 4.29–4.33).

8 Derive percentiles for a distribution by graphical methods and by calculation, using ungrouped data (paragraphs 6.8–6.11).

9 Derive quartiles from ungrouped data (paragraphs 5.6–5.10).

10 Explain the terms inter-quartile range, quartile deviation and inter-quartile ratio (paragraphs 5.6–5.10, 5.29–5.30).

11 Calculate the variance for a frequency distribution using ungrouped data (paragraphs 5.11–5.16, 5.20–5.21).

12 Explain the meaning and use of the coefficient of variation (paragraphs 5.25–5.28).

13 Choose summary measures of location and dispersion for a frequency distribution which are appropriate for the level of measurement of the variable concerned (paragraphs 4.1–4.2, 4.26–4.35, 5.1–5.5, 5.10–5.15, 5.19, 5.23, 5.24).

14 Derive standard scores for a given set of data (paragraphs 6.2–6.7).

15 Plot a scatter diagram to show the relationship between two variables (paragraph 8.2).

16 Explain the notion of correlation between two variables (paragraph 8.1).

17 Given data in the form of a scatter diagram, identify high, low and zero correlation (paragraphs 8.4, 8.5).

18 Describe and calculate a measure of correlation for two variables when:

(a) both are measured on an interval or ratio scale (paragraphs 8.6, 8.12–8.14).

(b) both are measured on an ordinal scale (paragraphs 8.24–8.26).

(c) one is measured on a dichotomous nominal scale and the other on an interval or ratio scale (paragraphs 8.27–8.30).

(d) both are measured on a nominal scale and are dichotomous (paragraphs 8.31–8.37).

Appendix: Data Set

Case number	Occupation of father	Family income (£ per week)	Career	Number of children in household	Sex of child	Attitude of parents to part-time job	Child's ability score
01	4	18	1	3	1	3	42
02	2	32	1	2	2	3	60
03	4	26	1	2	1	4	70
04	3	30	2	1	2	4	60
05	5	19	2	4	1	1	66
06	6	9	1	7	2	2	26
07	1	41	2	1	1	1	80
08	4	21	1	2	2	2	52
09	2	24	2	3	1	2	14
10	4	20	1	3	2	1	30
11	1	35	2	3	2	5	49
12	4	18	0	3	2	2	44
13	4	17	2	3	1	2	33
14	4	25	1	2	2	3	64
15	2	26	0	5	1	1	58
16	2	31	1	2	1	5	21
17	5	13	0	4	1	1	39
18	6	15	2	2	1	2	51
19	4	31	2	1	1	2	93
20	4	28	2	2	2	4	86
21	2	28	1	1	2	5	32
22	4	23	2	3	1	3	45
23	4	19	1	3	2	2	46
24	3	16	2	4	1	2	47
25	3	14	0	6	2	2	71
26	4	16	1	5	1	2	27
27	5	22	0	2	2	3	72
28	4	20	0	2	1	1	55
29	5	16	1	4	2	3	58
30	5	12	0	5	2	1	9

Source: These data are a sample of cases from a follow-up survey carried out in 1968 of 2694 parents who were interviewed in a national survey conducted in 1964 for the Plowden Committee on Primary Education.

Notes

The Variable codes are as follows:

1 Occupation of father

Social Class I	1
Social Class II	2
Social Class III (Non-manual)	3
Social Class III (Manual)	4
Social Class IV	5
Social Class V	6

2   Income of family is given in £ per week.

3   Career

Child and parents agree on career	2
Child has career in mind, parent has not	1
Child and parents disagree on career	0

4   Number of children in household

One child	1
Two children	2
Three children	3
Four children	4
Five children	5
Six children	6
Seven children	7

5   Sex

Male	1
Female	2

6   Attitude of parent to part-time job for child

Strongly approves	1
Approves (on the whole)	2
Won't mind	3
Disapproves (on the whole)	4
Strongly disapproves	5

7   Child's ability score

This is a composite score from zero to 100 marks, derived from three separate tests.

Answers to Self-assessment Questions

SAQ 1

Ratio scale	– Family income
	– Number of children in household
	– Child's ability score
Interval scale	– None
Ordinal scale	– Occupation of father
	– Attitude of parents to part-time job
Nominal scale	– Sex of child
	– Career

SAQ 2

Frequency distribution of number of children in household

Number of children in household	Number or frequency f_i
1	4
2	9
3	8
4	4
5	3
6	1
7	1
Total	30

SAQ 3

Child's ability is scored from 0 to 100 and there are many possible ways of grouping the scores. Using intervals of 20 marks, we get the following table:

Grouped frequency distribution of child's ability score

Score	Frequency or number f_i
Under 20	2
20 but under 40	7
40 but under 60	11
60 but under 80	7
80 and over	3
Total	30

It so happens that these intervals give us a reasonable distribution with which to summarize the raw data. If we had required greater detail we could have used intervals of say 10 marks or even 5 marks.

SAQ 4

The variable 'employment position of mother' does not correspond to any single scale of measurement. It is a hybrid of nominal and ratio scales. Categories coded 1, 2, 3 represent a nominal scale, whereas categories coded 4, 5, 6, 7 represent a ratio scale.

Categories can be combined to produce a consistent scale: for example, categories 4, 5, 6, 7 could be combined to produce a single category which could be called 'mothers gainfully employed and working away from home'. Taken together with the other three categories, this would produce a single nominal scale.

A special kind of nominal scale variable which can only take one of two values is called a *dichotomy* or *dichotomous* variable. The present classification of Plowden mothers in terms of employment can be collapsed to produce a dichotomy. If all categories except the first are combined to create a new category of mothers gainfully employed, this produces a dichotomous nominal variable. The two categories 'Not gainfully employed' and 'Gainfully employed' are mutually exclusive and exhaustive, so they fulfil the requirements of a measurement scale; all mothers in the Plowden sample must fall in one or other of these categories and no mother can fall in both.

It is always possible to collapse categories on higher-order scales of measurement such as ratio and ordinal scales to produce new categories measured on an equivalent scale or a lower-order scale. It is never possible to expand a nominal scale to a higher-level scale such as ordinal, interval or ratio, unless the variable was originally measured at the higher level and the supplementary information is available.

SAQ 5

You may have suggested one or more of the following interpretations of Table 5:

(a)   The number of cases of 'fatherless families' is small (121) compared with 'both parents in family' (2731). One must be cautious in looking at the difference between the two groups because of this disparity.

(b)   Within both 'fatherless families' and 'both parents in family', the largest number of mothers fall in the 'not working' category.

(c)   Any further comparison between the two groups is very difficult without percentaging the columns as is shown in the text.

SAQ 6

Your answer should take the answer to SAQ 5 as its starting-point. Now that the table has been percentaged we can more easily compare the two groups of 'fatherless families' and 'both parents present'. Your answer may include all or some of the following points:

(a)   In fatherless families fewer mothers stay at home full-time, 46% as against 65% where both parents are present in the family.

(b)   The majority of mothers in families where both parents are present do not work, whereas for fatherless families nearly equal proportions work either full-time or not at all.

(c)   Over half of mothers on their own are at work, whereas only a third of mothers in families with both parents present work at all.

(d)   In fatherless families, the proportions of mothers polarize between not working at all or working full-time; few work part-time. In contrast, where both parents are present, there is a gradation from mothers not working, through mothers working part-time, to the least common category of mothers working full-time.

Notice (i) that these conclusions *compare* the two groups; (ii) that the written conclusions have translated 'away from home under 5 hours per day' and 'away from home more than 5 hours per day' into part-time or full-time work respectively. This is to make the statements easier to read. Any new categories should always be very carefully defined, so a footnote explaining the meaning of full- and part-time work is required here; (iii) a researcher would start thinking of explanations for the patterns in the table. The one which is of most interest (because unexpected) is that in conclusion (d) above, and one could, for example, look at the operation of social security payments to part-time workers. But this is not a conclusion drawn *from* the table, it represents the next set of questions to ask.

SAQ 7

(a)   For the number of children in household we can begin with the frequency distribution found in the answer to SAQ 2.

Frequency distribution

Number of children in household	Frequency	Relative frequency %
1	4	13
2	9	30
3	8	27
4	4	13
5	3	10
6	1	3
7	1	3
Total	30	99[1]

Note   [1]The percentages add to 99 because of rounding errors

Cumulative and cumulative relative frequency distribution

Number of children	Cumulative frequency	Cumulative relative frequency %
1 or less	4	13
2 or less	13	43
3 or less	21	70
4 or less	25	83
5 or less	28	93
6 or less	29	97
7 or less	30	100

Notice that we could have cumulated by taking the categories, 1 or more, 2 or more, 3 or more, etc. as follows:

Number of children	Cumulative frequency	Cumulative relative frequency %
1 or more	30	100
2 or more	26	87
3 or more	17	57
4 or more	9	30
5 or more	5	17
6 or more	2	6
7 or more	1	3

(b) For child ability score we can begin with the answer to SAQ 3.

Frequency distribution

Scores	Frequency
Under 20	2
20 but under 40	7
40 but under 60	11
60 but under 80	7
80 and over	3
Total	30

Cumulative and cumulative relative frequency distribution

Scores	Cumulative frequency	Cumulative relative frequency %
Under 20	2	7
Under 40	9	30
Under 60	20	67
Under 80	27	90
All	30	100

SAQ 8

(a) Frequency distribution for the variable 'child's career'

Code	Career	Frequency f_i	Relative frequency %
2	Child and parents agree on career	11	37
1	Child has career in mind, parent has not	12	40
0	Child and parents disagree on career	7	23
Total		30	100

(b) Bar-chart for the above table

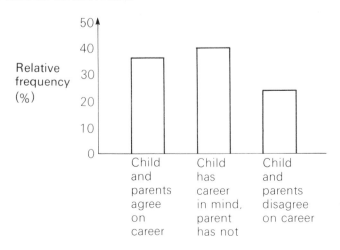

SAQ 9

(a) Attitude of parents to part-time jobs by sex of child

Attitude of parent	Boys		Girls	
	Frequency	Relative frequency %	Frequency	Relative frequency %
Strongly approves	5	33	2	13
Approves	6	40	5	33
Won't mind	2	13	4	27
Disapproves	1	7	2	13
Strongly disapproves	1	7	2	13
Total	15	100	15	99[1]

Note   [1] The percentages add to 99 due to rounding errors

(b) Bar-chart for the above table

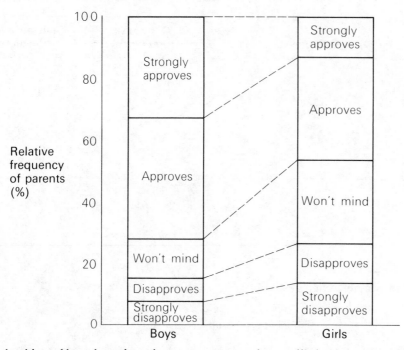

Both table and bar-chart show that parents are much more likely to approve of part-time jobs for boys and disapprove of them for girls.

SAQ 10

(a) Frequency distribution of family income

Family income (£ per week)	Frequency	Relative frequency %	Width of class interval	Relative frequency/ Interval
(i)	(ii)	(iii)	(iv)	$(v) = \dfrac{(iii)}{(iv)}$
£7.50 but under £10	1	3	2.5[1]	1.2
£10 but under £12.50	1	3	2.5	1.2
£12.50 but under £15	2	7	2.5	2.8
£15 but under £20	9	30	5	6.0
£20 but under £25	6	20	5	4.0
£25 but under £30	5	17	5	3.4
£30 but under £40	5	17	10	1.7
£40 and over	1	3	10[1]	0.3
Total	30	100		

Note   [1] The first interval has been assumed to be £7.50 but under £10, and the last interval to be £40 but under £50.

(b)   Histogram for the above distribution

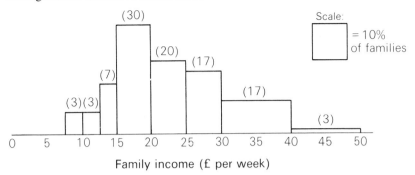

Family income (£ per week)

Note   The figures in parentheses above each block correspond to the relative frequencies represented by the block

SAQ 11

Yes, because the intention in representing a grouped frequency distribution in the form of a histogram is that the *area* of each block of the diagram should represent the relative frequency of each group in the distribution. If the class intervals for each group are all equal in width, then the relative areas of each block will be directly proportional to their relative heights, and so the height of each block will directly represent the relative frequency of that group.

(a)   Relative frequency distribution for family income

Family income (£ per week)	Frequency	Relative frequency %
Under £10	1	3
£10 but under £15	3	10
£15 but under £20	9	30
£20 but under £25	6	20
£25 but under £30	5	17
£30 but under £35	4	13
£35 but under £40	1	3
£40 and over	1	3
Total	30	99[1]

Note   [1] The percentages add to 99 because of rounding

If we assume that the first interval in the table is '£5 but under £10' and the last is '£40 but under £45', then all the intervals are of equal width. In this case the heights of the blocks in a histogram can be made equal to or proportional to the frequency or relative frequency as shown below.

(b)   Histogram for the above table

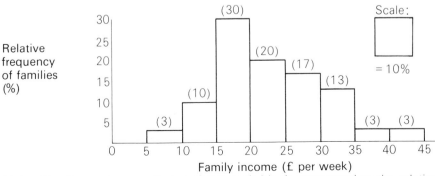

Note   The figures in parentheses above each block correspond to the relative frequencies represented by the block

SAQ 12

(a)   Cumulative relative frequency distribution for family income

Family income (£ per week)	Cumulative relative frequency %
Under £10	3
Under £15	13
Under £20	43
Under £25	63
Under £30	80
Under £35	93
Under £40	96
All	99

Note   The percentages add to 99 because of rounding

(b)   Ogive for the above distribution

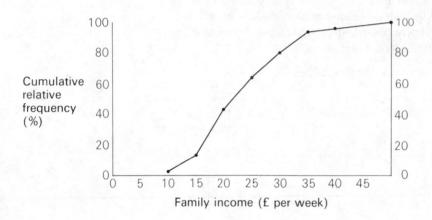

SAQ 13

The frequency distribution of the four variables are as follows:

(a) Occupation of father	Frequency
Social Class I	2
II	5
III (NM)	3
III (M)	13
IV	5
V	2
Total	30

(b) Number of children in household	Frequency
1	4
2	9
3	8
4	4
5	3
6	1
7	1
Total	30

(c) Attitude of parents to part-time job	Frequency
Strongly approves	7
Approves	11
Won't mind	6
Disapproves	3
Strongly disapproves	3
Total	30

(d) Career	Frequency
Child and parents agree on career	11
Child has career in mind, parent has not	12
Child and parents disagree on career	7
Total	30

Thus the model categories are:

(a) Social Class III (Manual) with 13 out of a total of 30 cases.

(b) 2 children in household with 9 out of 30 cases.

(c) Approves, with a total of 11 out of 30 cases.

(d) Child has career in mind, parent has not, with a total of 12 cases out of 30.

Note From your answer to SAQ 1 notice that the four variables here represent three levels of measurement; 'career' is a nominal variable, 'attitude' and 'occupation' are ordinal variables and 'number of children' is a ratio variable.

SAQ 14

The first eight incomes are (in £ per week):

$$18 \ 32 \ 26 \ 30 \ 19 \ 9 \ 41 \ 21$$

These have now to be placed in rank order:

$$9 \ 18 \ 19 \ 21 \ 26 \ 30 \ 32 \ 41$$

With 8 observations the median income lies between the income of the fourth and fifth observation in rank order.
Thus it is halfway between £21 and £26, $\tilde{X} = £23.50$.

SAQ 15

The cumulative frequency distribution for the number of children in household is given below:

Number of children in household	Frequency	Cumulative frequency
1	4	4
2	9	13
3	8	21
4	4	25
5	3	28
6	1	29
7	1	30
Total	30	

With 30 observations the median number of children in household is that which lies between the 15th and 16th in rank order. Thus,

$$\tilde{X} = 3 \text{ children in household}$$

Compare this with the value obtained for the mode (2 children in household) (SAQ 13).

SAQ 16

(a) Family income
The family incomes for the first 10 cases (in £ per week) are:

$$18 \ 32 \ 26 \ 30 \ 19 \ 9 \ 41 \ 21 \ 24 \ 20$$

The sum of these incomes is:

$$\Sigma X_i = (18 + 32 + 26 + 30 + 19 + 9 + 41 + 21 + 24 + 20)$$
$$= 240$$

The number of observations, $n = 10$.
Then the arithmetic mean is:

$$\overline{X} = \frac{\text{Sum of values}}{\text{Number of observations}} = \frac{\Sigma X_i}{n} = \frac{240}{10}$$
$$= £24 \text{ per week}$$

Compare this with the median value of £23.50 for these ten observations (SAQ 14). No mode exists.

(b)   Child's ability score

The children's ability scores for the first 10 cases are:

$$42 \ 60 \ 70 \ 60 \ 66 \ 26 \ 80 \ 52 \ 14 \ 30$$

The sum of these scores is:

$$\Sigma Y_i = (42 + 60 + 70 + 60 + 66 + 26 + 80 + 52 + 14 + 30)$$
$$= 500$$

The number of observation, $n = 10$.

Then the arithmetic mean is:

$$\overline{Y} = \frac{\text{Sum of values}}{\text{Number of observations}} = \frac{\Sigma Y_i}{n} = \frac{500}{10}$$
$$= 50 \text{ marks}$$

Notice that the letter 'Y' has been used to stand for the variable instead of the letter 'X'. This makes absolutely no difference to the calculation.

Compare the value of 50 marks for the mean of these ten observations with a median value of 56 marks and a (meaningless) mode of 60 marks.

SAQ 17

Number of children in household X_i (i)	Frequency f_i (ii)	$f_i X_i$ (iii)
1	4	4
2	9	18
3	8	24
4	4	16
5	3	15
6	1	6
7	1	7
Total	30	90

Thus the arithmetic mean of the number of children in household is given by:

$$\overline{X} = \frac{1}{n} \Sigma f_i X_i = \frac{90}{30}$$
$$= 3 \text{ children in household}$$

The median is also 3 children but the mode is 2 children in household.

SAQ 18
(a) Family income

X_i (i)	$(X_i - \overline{X})$ (ii)	Negative differences	Positive differences
19	− 5	− 5	
32	+ 8		+ 8
26	+ 2		+ 2
30	+ 6		+ 6
18	− 6	− 6	
9	− 15	− 15	
41	+ 17		+ 17
21	− 3	− 3	
24	0		
20	− 4	− 4	
$\Sigma(X_i - \overline{X}) = 0$		− 33	+ 33

The first ten cases of family income are listed in column (i). We know that the arithmetic mean of family income is $\bar{X} = 24$. The sum of the differences $(X_i - \bar{X})$ can be seen to be zero.

(b)   Child's ability score

Y_i (i)	$(Y_i - \bar{Y})$ (ii)	Negative differences	Positive differences
42	− 8	− 8	
60	+ 10		+ 10
70	+ 20		+ 20
60	+ 10		+ 10
66	+ 16		+ 16
26	− 24	− 24	
80	+ 30		+ 30
52	+ 2		+ 2
14	− 36	− 36	
30	− 20	− 20	
$\Sigma (Y_i - \bar{Y}) = 0$		− 88	+ 88

The first tendencies of children's ability scores are shown in column (i). We know that the arithmetic mean is $\bar{Y} = 50$. The sum of the differences $(Y_i - \bar{Y})$ can be seen to be zero.

SAQ 19
(a)   The ability scores for boys are:

$$66 \quad 70 \quad 42 \quad 80 \quad 14$$

Thus, $n_b = 5$, and the sum of scores is $\Sigma Y_b = 272$.
Therefore, the mean score for boys is:

$$\bar{Y}_b = \frac{1}{n} \Sigma Y_b = \frac{272}{5}$$
$$= 54.4$$

(b)   The ability scores for girls are:

$$60 \quad 60 \quad 26 \quad 52 \quad 30$$

Thus, $n_g = 5$, and the sum of scores is $\Sigma Y_g = 228$.
Therefore, the mean score for girls is:

$$\bar{Y}_g = \frac{1}{n} \Sigma Y_g = \frac{228}{5}$$
$$= 45.6$$

(c)   The combined mean score for boys and girls is thus:

$$\bar{Y} = \frac{n_b \bar{Y}_b + n_g \bar{Y}_g}{n_b + n_g} = \frac{(5)(54.4) + (5)(45.6)}{5 + 5} = \frac{500}{10}$$
$$= 50$$

SAQ 20
(a)   The distribution of family income is positively skewed. The distribution of child's ability score is very nearly symmetrical.

(b)   In the distribution of family income, the mode (estimated as 17·5) is less than the median ($\tilde{X} = 21.5$), which is less than the mean ($\bar{X} = 25.7$). In the distribution of child's ability scores, the mode (estimated as 45) is less than the median ($\tilde{Y} = 50$) which is equal to the mean ($\bar{Y} = 50$). In fact the mode is smaller only because of the way in which the data are grouped and the equality of the mean and median confirms that the distribution is at least approximately symmetrical.

SAQ 21

In rank order the first eight cases of family income are:

$$9 \quad 18 \quad 19 \quad 21 \quad 26 \quad 30 \quad 32 \quad 41$$

With 8 cases, the lower quartile lies halfway between the 2nd and 3rd cases, i.e.

$$Q_1 = 18.5$$

The upper quartile lies halfway between the 6th and 7th cases, i.e.

$$Q_3 = 31$$

Thus the quartile deviation is:

$$QD = \frac{Q_3 - Q_1}{2} = \frac{31 - 18.5}{2} = \frac{12.5}{2}$$
$$= £6.25$$

In rank order the first eight cases of numbers of children in household are:

$$1 \quad 1 \quad 2 \quad 2 \quad 2 \quad 3 \quad 4 \quad 7$$

$$Q_1 = 1.5 \qquad\qquad\qquad\qquad Q_2 = 3.5$$

And,

$$QD = \frac{3.5 - 1.5}{2}$$
$$= 1 \text{ child}$$

SAQ 22

The child's ability score for the first ten cases are shown in column (i) below. The mean of these scores (from the answer to SAQ 16) is $\overline{Y} = 50$. Column (ii) shows the deviation of each score from its mean and column (iii) the absolute value of the deviation.

X_i (i)	$(Y_i - \overline{Y})$ (ii)	$\|(Y_i - \overline{Y})\|$ (iii)
14	− 36	36
26	− 24	24
30	− 20	20
42	− 8	8
52	+ 2	2
60	+ 10	10
60	+ 10	10
66	+ 16	16
70	+ 20	20
80	+ 30	30
	$\Sigma\|(Y_i - \overline{Y})\| = 176$	

The mean deviation is therefore given by:

$$MD = \frac{1}{n}\Sigma|(Y_i - \overline{Y})| = \frac{176}{10}$$
$$= 17.6$$

The mean for this distribution of ten scores is 50 with a mean deviation of 17.6 marks.

SAQ 23

The child's ability score for the first ten cases are shown in column (i) below. The mean of these scores (from the answer to SAQ 16) is $\overline{Y} = 50$. Column (ii) shows the deviation of each score from its mean and column (iii) the square of these deviations.

Y_i (i)	$(Y_i - \overline{Y})$ (ii)	$(Y_i - \overline{Y})^2$ (iii)
14	− 36	1296
26	− 24	576
30	− 20	400
42	− 8	64
52	+ 2	4
60	+ 10	100
60	+ 10	100
66	+ 16	256
70	+ 20	400
80	+ 30	900
		$\Sigma(Y_i - \overline{Y})^2 = 4096$

Thus, the variance is:

$$s_y^2 = \frac{1}{n}\Sigma(Y_i - \overline{Y})^2 = \frac{4096}{10}$$

$$= 409.6$$

and the standard deviation is:

$$s_y = \sqrt{\frac{1}{n}(Y_i - \overline{Y})^2} = \sqrt{409.6}$$

$$\simeq 20.2$$

The mean for this distribution of ten scores is 50 with a standard deviation of 20.2 marks.

SAQ 24

The child's ability score for the first ten cases are shown in column (i) below. The mean of these scores (from the answer to SAQ 16) is $\overline{Y} = 50$. Column (ii) shows the square of the scores.

Y_i (i)	Y_i^2 (ii)
14	196
26	676
30	900
42	1764
52	2704
60	3600
60	3600
66	4356
70	4900
80	6400
$\Sigma(Y_i)^2 =$	29096

Thus the variance is:

$$s_y^2 = \frac{1}{n}\Sigma Y_i^2 - \overline{Y}^2 = \frac{29\,096}{10} - (50)^2 = 2909.6 - 2500$$

$$= 409.6$$

The standard deviation is:

$$s_y = \sqrt{\frac{1}{n}\Sigma Y_i^2 - \overline{Y}^2} = \sqrt{409.6}$$

$$= 20.2$$

Note that the answers are the same as for the answers to SAQ 23.

SAQ 25

To find the coefficient of variation of family income for the first ten cases we need to know the arithmetic mean and standard deviation of the scores. These are calculated below:

X_i (i)	X_i^2 (ii)
9	81
18	324
19	361
20	400
21	441
24	576
26	676
30	900
32	1024
41	1681
$\Sigma X_i = 240$	$\Sigma X_i^2 = 6464$

Thus the arithmetic mean is:

$$\bar{X} = \frac{1}{n} \Sigma X_i = \frac{1}{10} \cdot 240$$
$$= £24$$

The standard deviation is:

$$s_x = \sqrt{\frac{1}{n} \Sigma X_i^2 - \bar{X}^2} = \sqrt{\frac{6464}{10} - (24)^2}$$

$$= \sqrt{646.4 - 576} = \sqrt{70.4}.$$

$$= 8.4$$

Therefore the coefficient of variation is:

$$cV = \frac{s_x}{\bar{X}} = \frac{8.4}{24}$$
$$= 0.35 \text{ or } 35\%$$

SAQ 26

In answering this question you should be clear about the information contained in Table 21. The Plowden researchers collected information on a number of variables which are shown in the left-hand column and the information was collected from primary and secondary schools for local authorities in England. Table 21 shows the values of the cV for the distribution of each variable amongst local authorities, separately for primary and secondary schools. So, for example, the value of 7.2 for the distribution of 'Expenditure on teachers' salaries per pupil', shows that for this distribution the standard deviation was about 7% of the mean value of the distribution. This is quite a low figure which might be expected since teachers' salaries are fixed nationally and there is little scope for variation between local authorities. This value of 7% is much lower than for any other variable except 'Total cost per pupil' which, of course, includes teachers' salaries. The values of the cV for teachers' salaries are identical for primary and secondary schools which is also, perhaps, not very surprising considering the great majority of teachers will be on the same salary scale regardless of type of school.

If you compare the values of the cV between primary and secondary schools for each variable you will see there is not much difference except for the distribution of oversize classes. Clearly there is much more variability across the country in the distribution of this variable in primary schools than in secondary schools.

The variable which has the greatest dispersion in terms of the cV for both primary and secondary schools is 'Teachers released for special advanced training', which suggests that there is very wide variation between local authorities on this variable. Otherwise, apart from the low cV for teachers' salaries, the distributions of all the other variables seem similar in terms of dispersion about the mean.

SAQ 27

The median family income $\tilde{X} = 23.50$ and the inter-quartile range $= 12.5$. Thus the inter-quartile ratio is:

$$IQR = \frac{Q_3 - Q_1}{\tilde{X}} = \frac{12.5}{23.5}$$
$$= 0.53 \text{ or } 53\%$$

SAQ 28

Table 22 shows that, in terms of the inter-quartile ratio, the relative dispersion of income for households owning their property outright is more than twice that for householders owning their property with mortgage. Indeed mortgagees are a much more homogeneous group in terms of income than are any other group of householders. This could be something to do with the loan allocation policies of Building Societies. Those householders owning their property outright are most heterogeneous in terms of income. Household income of those renting from local authorities is more heterogeneous than of those buying on mortgage but more homogeneous than those renting private unfurnished accommodation.

Median household income is highest for those buying on mortgage but the IQR is least, so these households represent middle income groups. Median incomes for households renting privately and owning their property outright are least and next lowest respectively, so some of the lowest income households in Great Britain must be represented in these two tenure categories. (The category of those owning outright probably includes a high proportion of retired people.) But these are the two categories with greatest dispersion coefficient, so some of the highest income households in Great Britain must be represented there too. Median household income for local authority tenants is rather less than that for households buying with mortgage, but the dispersion of incomes is just a little greater.

So, the eight figures in Table 22 contain a lot of information and may suggest hypotheses about the social structure of housing in Britain and about housing allocation policies and procedures in the public and private sectors. Clearly much subsidiary information is also relevant to a fuller consideration of these data.

SAQ 29

The number of children in household for the first four cases in the data set is given in column (i). Column (ii) shows the square of these values. Column (iii) shows the deviation of each value in column (i) from the mean, $\bar{X} = 2$, and column (iv) shows column (iii) divided by the standard deviation of the values, i.e. column (iv) gives

$$z_i = \frac{X_i - \bar{X}}{s_x}$$

Column (v) shows the square of the z_i values.

X_i	X_i^2	$(X_i - \bar{X})$	$z_i = \dfrac{X_i - \bar{X}}{s_x}$	z_i^2
(i)	(ii)	(iii)	(iv)	(v)
1	1	-1	-1.4	2
2	4	0	0	0
2	4	0	0	0
3	9	$+1$	$+1.4$	2
$\Sigma X_i = 8$	$\Sigma X_i^2 = 18$	$\Sigma(X_i - \bar{X}) = 0$	$\Sigma z_i = 0$	$\Sigma z_i^2 = 4$

First we need to calculate the arithmetic mean:

$$\bar{X} = \frac{1}{n} \Sigma X_i = \frac{8}{4}$$
$$= 2$$

Then the standard deviation is:

$$s_x = \sqrt{\frac{1}{n} \Sigma X_i^2 - (\bar{X})^2} = \sqrt{\frac{18}{4} - (2)^2}$$
$$= \sqrt{4.5 - 4} = \sqrt{0.5}$$
$$= 0.7$$

Thus, from column (iv) we find that the mean of the z_i scores is:

$$\bar{z} = \frac{1}{n} \Sigma z_i = \frac{1}{4} \cdot 0$$
$$= 0$$

and from column (v) we find that the standard deviation of the z_i scores is:

$$s_z = \sqrt{\frac{1}{n} \Sigma z_i^2 - (\bar{z})^2} = \sqrt{\frac{1}{4} \cdot 4 - (0)^2} = \sqrt{\frac{4}{4}}$$
$$= 1$$

Thus, for these data we can see that the mean of the z-scores is zero and the standard deviation is unity. This is *always* the case with *any* set of numbers.

SAQ 30

Number of children in household	Cumulative relative frequency distribution %
1	13
2	43
3	70
4	83
5	93
6	97
7	100

Number of children in household is a discrete variable taking only whole number values and it does not make sense to estimate fractional values for the percentiles. Also, with only 30 cases in the data set, it is not possible to estimate values for each percentile.

Thus: the 20th percentile corresponds to 2 children per household
the 60th percentile corresponds to 3 children per household
the 90th percentile corresponds to 5 children per household
and the 95th percentile corresponds to 5 children per household.

SAQ 31

The median score increased from 11.3 to 14.7. In other words in 1948 half the pupils scored 11.3 or better but in 1964 half the pupils scored 14.7 or better. Also, in 1964 a total of 70% of pupils scored 11.3 or better. In 1964 only 10% of pupils scored 7.5 or less whereas in 1948 about 25% scored 7.5 or less. In 1948 only 10% of pupils scored 18.4 or more whereas in 1964 30% of pupils scored 18.4 or more.

Many similar statements could be made. In addition we can calculate that in 1948 the quartile deviation was approximately 3.8 and the inter-quartile ratio about 34%, but in 1964 the quartile deviation was 4.5 and the inter-quartile ratio about 31%. Thus, the relative dispersion in the distribution of marks on reading comprehension had decreased, or, in other words, the gap between ablest and weakest child had narrowed (relatively) whilst overall performance had increased.

SAQ 32

Several conclusions can be drawn from Table 24, among them are the following. The lower half of all earners received 24.2% of total earnings, the other half received the remaining 75.8% of earnings. The bottom 10% of earners received only 2.7% of earnings, whereas the top 10% received 26.8% of earnings. The top 1% received 6.5% of earnings, more than twice the total amount received by the bottom 10%.

80% of all earners received between £549 and £3260 before tax, and only 1% received more than £7195 but 10% received less than £549.

SAQ 33

There are more male heads than female heads in all schools except purely infant schools: in Infant/Junior schools there are almost twice as many male heads as female heads; in Junior schools there are over seven times as many male heads and in Secondary Modern schools there are over four times as many male heads; but in purely Infant schools there are only three male heads for every hundred female heads. However, in purely Infant schools there is only one male assistant teacher for every hundred female assistant teachers, so male Infant school teachers have three times the prospects of gaining headship than their female colleagues. This male bias in favour of headships is common to every type of school in the table. Sex ratios for heads are much higher than for assistants. So Table 25 shows that in Junior and Secondary Modern Schools the teaching profession is male dominated and for all types of school the prospects of promotion are better for male assistant teachers.

In discussing tables of data such as this, you should *always* take into account the source of the data and any qualifications or notes provided. In this particular case the data derive from a survey of teachers and the response rate was approximately 75%, i.e. 25% of teachers did not reply to the questionnaire. A problem arises if the rate of non-response is different for men and women. The sex ratios in the survey sample will then not correspond to those in the wider population of teachers. For the data shown in Table 25 it is not possible to say whether the results have been affected by differential non-response rates between men and women teachers, because the relevant information is not given in the Plowden Report. But we do know that 25% of the total sample did not respond. Suppose these 25% were all women teachers – unlikely, but how would that affect the results, do you think? Even more unlikely, suppose all the non-respondents had been women head teachers, how would the results then have been affected? If either of these two situations obtained then the survey results would be biased. It is true, these two hypothetical situations *are* unlikely, but the fact is, we just do not know to what extent the non-response has led to a biased result. These issues will be returned to in Block 3, Part 4, 'Introduction to Applied Sampling'.

SAQ 34

(a)   Scatter diagram for child's ability score (*Y*) and family income (*X*) for the first ten cases.

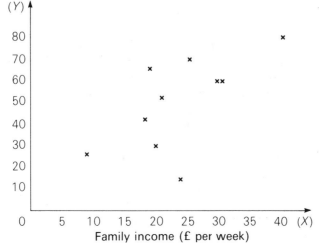

(b)   Scatter diagram for child's ability score (Y) and number of children in household (X) for the first ten cases.

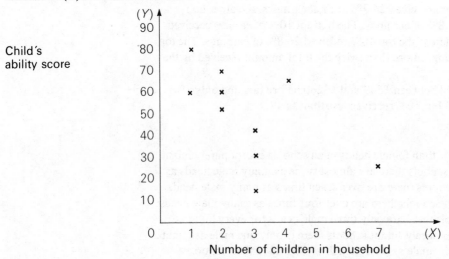

(c)   Scatter diagram for family income (Y) and number of children in household (X) for the first ten cases.

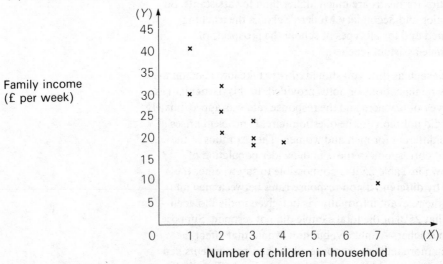

Thus in (a) the pattern provides evidence of a positive correlation with family income and score both increasing together.

In (b) the situation is more difficult but, given the small number of cases, it would seem best to say that there is not much evidence of a relationship between the child's score and the number of children in the household.

In (c) there is a definite negative relationship where high family income is associated with a low number of children in household, and *vice versa*.

SAQ 35

In the table below, column (i) shows the family income (X_i) and column (iii) the child's ability score (Y_i) for the first ten cases in the data set. From the answer to SAQ 16 we know the arithmetic mean of family income, $\bar{X} = £24$, and that of the children's ability score, $\bar{Y} = 50$. Thus columns (ii) and (iv) show the respective deviation from the means; and column (v) multiplies these deviations together.

The covariance between family income (X) and child's ability score (Y) is given by:

$$Cov = \frac{1}{n} \Sigma (X_i - \bar{X})(Y - \bar{Y}) = + \frac{1092}{10}$$
$$= + 109.2$$

Thus the covariance is positive which confirms the conclusion drawn from the scatter diagram in the answer to SAQ 34 (a). The value of the covariance is a

X_i (i)	$(X_i - \overline{X})$ (ii)	Y_i (iii)	$(Y_i - \overline{Y})$ (iv)	$(X_i - \overline{X})(Y_i - \overline{Y})$ (v) = (ii) × (iv)
9	− 15	26	− 24	+ 360
18	− 6	42	− 8	+ 48
19	− 5	66	+ 16	− 80
20	− 4	30	− 20	+ 80
21	− 3	52	+ 2	− 6
24	0	14	− 36	0
26	+ 2	70	+ 20	+ 40
30	+ 6	60	+ 10	+ 60
32	+ 8	60	+ 10	+ 80
41	+ 17	80	+ 30	+ 510

$$\Sigma(X_i - \overline{X})(Y_i - \overline{Y}) = + 1092$$

large number, but, as discussed in paragraph 8.11 of the text, we cannot directly interpret this as implying either a 'strong' or a 'weak' association.

see para. 8.11

SAQ 36

The data are the same as those used in SAQ 35. Since the correlation coefficient is calculated by the covariance of the two variables, Cov, divided by the two standard deviations, we need to find Cov, s_x and s_y. The workings are shown in the table below.

X_i (i)	X_i^2 (ii)	Y_i (iii)	Y_i^2 (iv)	$X_i Y_i$ (v)
9	81	26	676	234
18	324	42	1764	756
19	361	66	4356	1254
20	400	30	900	600
21	441	52	2704	1092
24	576	14	196	336
26	676	70	4900	1820
30	900	60	3600	1800
32	1024	60	3600	1920
41	1681	80	6400	3280
240	6464	500	29096	13092

Thus we have

$$\overline{X} = \frac{1}{n}\Sigma X_i = \frac{240}{10}$$
$$= 24$$

and

$$\overline{Y} = \frac{1}{n}\Sigma Y_i = \frac{500}{10}$$
$$= 50$$

The covariance is given by:

$$Cov = \frac{1}{n}\Sigma X_i Y_i - (\overline{X})(\overline{Y}) = \frac{13092}{10} - (50)(24)$$
$$= 1309.2 - 1200$$
$$= + 109.2$$

(*Note* This is the same answer as was obtained in SAQ 35.)

The standard deviation of family income (X) is given by:

$$s_x = \sqrt{\frac{1}{n} \Sigma X_i^2 - (\overline{X})^2} = \sqrt{\frac{1}{10}(6464) - (24)^2}$$

$$= \sqrt{646.4 - 576} = \sqrt{70.4}$$

$$\simeq 8.4$$

The standard deviation of children's ability scores (Y) is given by:

$$s_y = \sqrt{\frac{1}{n} \Sigma Y_i^2 - (\overline{Y})^2} = \sqrt{\frac{1}{10}(29096) - (50)^2}$$

$$= \sqrt{2909.6 - 2500} = \sqrt{409.6}$$

$$\simeq 20.2$$

Thus the product moment correlation coefficient is:

$$r = \frac{Cov}{s_x s_y} = \frac{109.2}{(8.4)(20.2)} = \frac{109.2}{169.7}$$

$$= +0.64$$

As might be judged from the scatter diagram in the answer to SAQ 34 (a) the correlation is positive and moderately strong.

SAQ 37

You may have made some or all of the following points:

(a)   The purpose of the table is to see the degree of relationship (if any) between standards of provision within Local Education Authorities, and three 'output' indices, which attempt, crudely, to measure the success of students in staying on at school and entering Higher Education. The degree of relationship is measured by the correlation coefficient.

(b)   All the relationships are quite weak. The largest is that between costs of teacher salaries/pupil (row (i)) and the percentage of pupils staying on at school (column (i)) when $r = 0.32$.

(c)   Two relationships show a zero correlation.

(d)   As one might expect all relationships with oversize classes show a negative correlation, i.e. the higher the percentage of oversize classes in a Local Education Authority, then the lower relatively will be the percentage staying on and going into Higher Education.

SAQ 38

The value for the first six cases for 'father's occupation' and 'attitude of parents to part-time jobs' are shown in column (i) and (ii) respectively. The rank order of these data are shown in columns (iii) and (iv) respectively. Column (v) shows the difference between the rank order for each case on the two variables, i.e. D_i and column (vi) shows D_i^2.

(i)	(ii)	X_i (iii)	Y_i (iv)	$D_i = X_i - Y_i$ (v)	D_i^2 (vi)
4	3	3.5	3.5	0	0
2	3	1	3.5	−2.5	6.25
4	4	3.5	5.5	−2	4.00
3	4	2	5.5	−3.5	12.25
5	1	5	1	+4	16.00
6	2	6	2	+4	16.00.
					$\Sigma D_i^2 = 54.5$

The number of cases is $n = 6$, and

$$\Sigma D_i^2 = 54.5$$

Thus the rank correlation coefficient is:

$$r_s = 1 - \frac{6 \Sigma D_i^2}{n(n^2 - 1)} = 1 - \frac{6(54.5)}{6(36-1)}$$

$$= 1 - \frac{327}{210} = 1 - 1.56$$

$$= -0.56$$

Thus there is a modest negative relationship between occupation of father and attitude of parents to part-time jobs, i.e. the higher the social status of the father's job, the less likely are the parents willing to allow the child to take a part-time job.

SAQ 39

Here we need to find:

(a)   The arithmetic mean of all 10 child's ability scores: this is given in the answer to SAQ 16 as $\bar{Y} = 50$.

(b)   The arithmetic mean of the boys' ability scores: this is given in the answer to SAQ 19 as $\bar{Y}_b = 54.4$.

(c)   The standard deviation of all 10 child's ability scores: this is given in SAQ answer 23 as $s_y = 20.2$.

(d)   The number of cases, $n = 10$, the number of boys, $n_1 = 5$ and the number of girls, $n_0 = 5$.

Thus the point biserial correlation coefficient between sex of child and child's ability score is:

$$r_{pb} = \sqrt{\frac{n_1}{n_0}} \cdot \frac{(\bar{Y}_i - \bar{Y})}{s_y}$$

$$= \sqrt{\frac{5}{5}} \cdot \frac{(54.4 - 50)}{20.2} = \frac{4.4}{20.2}$$

$$= +0.22$$

Thus the relationship is positive, i.e. boys tend to have higher scores, but very weak.

SAQ 40

The contingency table is as follows:

			Father's social class (X)		
			Non-manual	Manual	
			1	0	
Ability of child (Y)	More able	1	3	3	6
	Less able	0	1	3	4
			4	6	10

and the value of Phi is given by:

$$\emptyset = \frac{9-3}{\sqrt{(6)(4)(4)(6)}} = \frac{6}{24} = +0.25$$

So there is some slight evidence of a positive association between father's social class and child's ability score.

References

BALDAMUS, W. (1969) 'Alienation, anomie and industrial accidents', in Wilson, M. J. (ed.) (1979) Ch. 6.

PLOWDEN REPORT (1967) *Children and their primary schools,* Central Advisory Council for Education (England), Vol. 1: Report, Vol. 2: Research and surveys, London, HMSO.

ROBINSON, W. S. (1950) 'Ecological correlations and the behavior of individuals', *American Sociological Review,* Vol. 15, pp. 351–7.

WILSON, M. J. (ed.) (1979) *Social and educational research in action: a book of readings,* London, Longman/The Open University Press (Course Reader).

Acknowledgements

Grateful acknowledgement is made to the following for permission to reproduce material in this Part of this Block:

Tables 5, 7, 8, 9, 10, 11, 21, 23, 25 and 29 from *Children and their primary schools,* (Plowden Report) Vol. 2, 1967, reproduced by permission of the Controller of HMSO; Table 24 and Figure 15 from *Royal Commission on the Distribution of Income and Wealth,* 2nd reprint, 1976, Cmnd 6626, reproduced by permission of the Controller of HMSO.

Notes

Notes

Notes

Notes